OXFORD
TEACHING GUIDES

Enhance Your Mathematics Subject Knowledge

Number & Algebra
for Secondary Teachers

JEMMA SHERWOOD

OXFORD

UNIVERSITY PRESS

Great Clarendon Street, Oxford, OX2 6DP, United Kingdom

Oxford University Press is a department of the University of Oxford.
It furthers the University's objective of excellence in research, scholarship, and
education by publishing worldwide. Oxford is a registered trade mark of Oxford
University Press in the UK and in certain other countries

British Library Cataloguing in Publication Data
Data available

978-0-19-842326-3

Kindle edition

978-0-19-842327-0

10 9 8 7 6 5 4 3 2

Paper used in the production of this book is a natural, recyclable product made
from wood grown in sustainable forests. The manufacturing process conforms to
the environmental regulations of the country of origin.

Printed and bound by CPI Group (UK) Ltd, Croydon, CR0 4YY

The Publisher would like to thank the following people for offering their
contribution in the development of this book: Elliot Galbraith, Gemma Medare,
Jo Morgan, Ben Hulme-Cross and Doug Forbes.

To Mum.

About the author

Jemma Sherwood has taught mathematics since 2004 in the West Midlands and Worcestershire (UK). In 2008, she became an Advanced Skills Teacher (AST), supporting teachers and mathematics leaders in numerous schools and, in the same year, she obtained a Master's degree in Mathematics Education. Jemma is now Head of Mathematics and a Specialist Leader of Education (SLE) in her school, where she currently  focuses on training teachers of other subjects who want to convert to teaching mathematics.

Jemma is a self-proclaimed mathematics obsessive who, when not teaching the subject, loves to read and write about it. She is particularly keen to encourage teachers continually to improve their subject knowledge, and wants her students to develop a love for mathematics that will follow them through life. Jemma's enthusiasm led her school to nominate her for the UK Teaching Awards and, in 2015, she was a Silver Award winner for *Teacher of the Year in a Secondary School.*

Jemma is married with two children. She has found herself particularly proud when one, at three-years-old, corrected a family member who called a rhombus a diamond; and the other, at five, requested toast cut 'like a sine wave'.

Contents

Acknowledgements

There are plenty of people without whom I would have had neither the experience nor the desire to write a book for mathematics teachers. I must start by saying thank you to my excellent teacher-trainers, Pat Perks and Dave Hewitt, who ignited my determination to understand mathematics properly and whose university sessions taught me to never settle for a poor explanation. Then there are the many wonderful teachers who have taught me so much along the way: Emma Partridge, Chris Gibbard, Caroline Hoddinott and many more. A special mention goes to Rob Bick, who taught me how to be precise and clear in the classroom, and has never, ever let me forget *that* stupid mistake!

Thank you to the people who have given me feedback on drafts of this book, in particular Elliot Galbraith, Gemma Medare and Jo Morgan, who helped to shape it into its final form, but also to the team at Oxford University Press, who didn't let me fall behind when there was so much else going on.

Finally, it is thanks to my husband David and the two most beautiful children in the world that I have been able to spend time writing. You really are the best, thank you for putting up with my educational obsessions.

Introduction

Mathematics and education

It was Gauss, one of the greatest mathematicians in history, who said that 'mathematics is the queen of the sciences [...] She often condescends to render service to astronomy and other natural sciences, but in all relations she is entitled to the first rank.' Mathematics is integral to science – not only to the natural sciences of chemistry, physics and biology, but also to engineering, computing, social science, medicine and more. You might call it the language through which science can be expressed and understood.

Yet mathematics is more than just its applications; it is 'entitled to the first rank'. In its own right, mathematics is an art form. Mathematicians solve problems, create problems, follow patterns, and play with numbers and shape in much the same way that a poet plays with words, or a painter experiments with colour and texture. It is the beauty to be found in mathematics for its own sake that has been the motivator of mathematicians through the centuries, many of whom could not have foreseen the later uses of their work.

The Oxford mathematician G.H. Hardy wrote, in the early twentieth century, that 'nothing [he had] ever done is of the slightest practical use', but he continued his work all the same, since he did not feel that mathematics had to justify itself by practical application. It turns out that his field of work – number theory – has a great many uses, not least in modern computing and internet security, but none of these uses was the driver for Hardy. Like so many before and after him, Hardy pursued mathematics for the intellectual challenge, for the love of the subject, and because he wanted to discover more about the world.

Mathematicians both create and describe, and what they do seems to be infinitely extendable: those who take on the work of others often find uses for it that the originator could never have dreamed of. When Fermat and Pascal started to work on the ideas of probability, they could not know how those ideas would one day be used to predict the weather or to develop life-saving drugs. When ancient mathematicians discovered sine and cosine, they would never have dreamed of how the study of waves would lead to modern communication methods.

Although the application of mathematics isn't what makes it important, it is in these applications that mathematics sets itself apart from poetry and painting. It is these applications that make complex and sometimes esoteric ideas accessible to everyone, even if only via the final result of the ideas, and it is these applications that cement mathematics' place on the school curriculum as an essential part of a modern education that gives our children access to the knowledge that has built our world while equipping them with the tools to find their own successful place in it. Some of them will become mathematicians, some will use mathematics in their job, many more will not directly use anything other than numerical skills, but all will inhabit a world built with mathematics, and all will benefit from having their understanding of the world improved through study of the subject.

Mathematics teachers, then, have a central role in our education system. Unfortunately in the UK and other Western nations we are in short supply. Large numbers of schools in England, for instance, have to enlist teachers of other subjects to staff their mathematics lessons. Many of these teachers do well, often with nothing more than a basic qualification in the subject, but do not always have the subject knowledge required to teach in depth. I have been privileged to have run a course for the past three years for so-called 'non-specialist' teachers and have worked with plenty of very enthusiastic people who will openly admit that they are often only one step ahead of the students. I feel very grateful for these dedicated colleagues, while sad that we find ourselves in this position in the first place.

Teachers' subject knowledge

Excellent mathematics teachers share many attributes: they know how to manage a classroom full of teenagers; they know how people learn and retain information; they know about mathematical pedagogy and how to effectively teach what can be very abstract ideas; and they have strong knowledge and understanding of mathematics, which drives the overall direction of their teaching as well as the minutiae of every lesson. With strong subject knowledge a teacher can stretch or simplify material as necessary, they can draw out or anticipate misconceptions, and they can provide students with the depth of understanding that will make them successful in and (hopefully) enthusiastic about our wonderful subject.

Yet it is very easy to think that your subject knowledge is better than it is. I trained to teach mathematics well over a decade ago, coming onto the training course with a first class degree in mathematics (and Russian, but that's another story). I thought I knew everything there was to know about school mathematics, I could remember how to 'do it all' and wasn't expecting to learn anything new. Oh, how wrong I was! On my course interview I was asked why we 'flip the second fraction and multiply' when dividing two fractions. That threw me. I'd always just done it, quite confidently, and knew that it worked. It had never dawned on me to consider *why* it worked.

There was plenty more. My mental arithmetic was a little sluggish, as I had spent years working with letters and not numbers. I took final-year modules in chaos theory and fluid dynamics, but I'd never stopped to properly consider the difference between an *equation*, an *expression*, and a *formula*. I'd never been taught long division and didn't know the link between trigonometry and similar triangles. The reason I didn't know these things is because I had never *needed* to. I was very successful in mathematics throughout school without knowing them and once I left school I moved on.

The result was someone with good qualifications, who was good at mathematics, but who didn't know all the intricacies and wouldn't yet be able to teach the subject really well. I didn't want to get caught out by a sharp student, I didn't want to be sloppy over my use of terminology, and I didn't want to *ever* be faced with an exam question that I struggled to answer because of gaps in my knowledge. Moreover, I knew that if I wanted my students to think hard in lessons, I needed to know how to challenge them, and I could only do that if I knew my stuff inside and out, the *why* as well as the *how*.

Over the years I have been teaching I have seen numerous new and trainee teachers make mistakes or struggle with different areas of school mathematics. These are people with degrees in mathematics, engineering, economics, computing and science who are good at mathematics. Sometimes there's a topic that wasn't on their school curriculum, so they have never learned it themselves. More often there are intricacies that they have never considered, having (as I had) moved on to 'harder mathematics'. In all cases they have spent a good few years having to improve and hone their subject knowledge in order to teach really well. In fact, improving your subject knowledge is something that never really stops.

I hope that some of this rings true with you. You might be a trainee mathematics teacher with a mathematics degree, like I was, but it is also likely that you have a degree in something related, such as engineering or economics. If that is the case, then you will be used to applying advanced mathematics but you may not have thought in much detail about the underlying structure of mathematical ideas, or how certain topics outside your specialism can be taken to greater depth. You might be one of those fabulous Physical Education or Geography or language teachers who has agreed to teach mathematics because there is no-one else to do so. If you are a teacher who wants to enhance their subject knowledge, please keep reading.

Origins

With all this in mind, I decided in 2016 that I wanted to write a book, one that would have benefitted me in my earlier years as a teacher. I wanted to record the things that I have seen trip up teachers, and the more obscure knowledge that you don't pick up when you are a student yourself, including interesting elements of the history of mathematics and the origins of some of the notation and ideas we take for granted. These ideas are often missing from mathematics classrooms, but they help us to place what we are doing in the broader picture.

I also wanted to give new teachers routes they could follow to develop their knowledge even more, with mathematics that isn't explicitly on, but is related to, the curriculum. While you are reading you might come across something you have never seen before that sparks your interest. Pursuing these ideas draws us further into the beauty of mathematics and helps us to develop a love for the subject that is infectious.

This book is written for anyone new to teaching mathematics, whether they are a trainee or a teacher of another subject, and for any teacher who wants to enhance their subject knowledge. The text and questions are for teachers rather than students, with the express aim of making you think more deeply about what you teach. The book does not stick rigidly to a particular course or curriculum. It touches a little on pedagogy, normally by asking you to discuss certain ideas with colleagues or by mentioning common mistakes that students make, but is predominantly focused on the teacher's mathematical knowledge as the bedrock of their classroom practice.

It is important to state that this book cannot contain All There Is to Know. At times, I have had to exclude things, and have by no means suggested all possible ideas for further exploration of topics. As I was writing, the book started to get too large, so I had to find a cut-off point; as much as it is possible to separate branches of mathematics, I have restricted the book to 'Number' and 'Algebra'.

Using this book

This book doesn't teach you how to do school mathematics. It assumes, for instance, that you know the correct order of operations, or how to solve a quadratic equation. There are times when certain algorithms are explained or set out, but this is to help you think about why things work, not to learn how to do them. It also introduces ideas beyond school mathematics, but which are accessible with school mathematics. Topics such as continued fractions or the golden ratio are included in the spirit of enhancing your subject knowledge but you are unlikely to teach them in the classroom.

The book is split into four chapters – two on number, two on algebra – and sections to break down topics a little more. The order of topics has been chosen deliberately so, for instance, the content of Chapter 4 does build on earlier chapters; however, it would be possible to take parts of the book in isolation – you don't have to tackle it in one go. To this end, the book starts with elements of number, such as place value, that you might think are straightforward. But be careful – there might be something that catches you out or that you had never thought of before.

All emboldened terms within the text are defined in the Glossary at the end of the book, and the following features are used throughout.

 Try this first

Each section starts with questions designed as prompts for your thinking, to prime you before you delve into the text.

 Preparing to teach – do the mathematics!

Try these questions yourself before proceeding

Grab a pencil and paper and give these problems a try. Some are short, some are long, some reinforce the reading before them, some get you to join up several ideas, some touch on ideas outside the curriculum but within the topic in question. All of them are meant to make you think.

 Discuss

Bigger questions on pedagogy that need talking through with others.

 Further exploration

Ideas or prompts suggesting how you might explore a topic some more.

 Thinking about the classroom

Sometimes these will give you an idea to try; sometimes they will warn you of common mistakes and misconceptions you ought to be prepared for.

As a teacher of mathematics, I know that reading about mathematics is never quite as useful as practising it. Each of the four chapters ends with a longer quiz; all the answers to the quizzes and problem boxes are at the back of the book. There will be some you find easy, some harder – it depends on where your strengths lie at the moment – and you may choose to use some in the classroom. The more you practise mathematics yourself, the more you will get from it. Don't stop with this book – there are plenty of recreational and popular mathematics books on the market from fantastic authors.

We spend our careers refining our subject knowledge along with every other aspect of our practice. We never stop learning and our own understanding improves year in, year out. I hope that if you read this book it will help you along your way a little more quickly and that you will be rewarded for the time you invest in it. Good luck on your journey as a mathematics teacher.

Jemma Sherwood
June 2018

Timeline of key mathematical events

Date and Place	Event
19th century BCE *Babylonia*	Babylonians use a base-60 numeral system.
11th century BCE *India*	The Hindu text the *Yajur Veda* discusses infinity.
6th century BCE *Italy*	Pythagoras and the Pythagoreans study geometry and rational numbers.
5th century BCE *Italy*	Zeno writes his paradoxes, which give an insight into the nature of infinity and 0.
c.300 BCE *Alexandria*	Euclid writes *Elements*, one of the most influential mathematical works of all time. In addition to geometry this early text book includes a definition of prime numbers, proof of the infinity of the primes and ideas on rational and irrational numbers.
c.250 BCE *Sicily*	Archimedes writes *Measurement of a Circle* in which he approximates π and square roots.
2nd century BCE *China*	*Nine Chapters on the Mathematical Art* is written, containing work on geometry, number and algebra: an approximation for π, Pythagoras's Theorem, square and cube roots, division, solving simultaneous equations, negative numbers and more.
c.250 CE *Alexandria*	Diophantus writes *Arithmetica*, a work on algebra which uses symbols and discusses solving different types of equations.
3rd century CE *Central America*	Mayans use a base-20 numeral system.
3rd century CE *India*	The Bakhshali manuscript is written, containing a symbol for 0, number sequences, fractions, square roots, and solving equations (linear, quadratic and simultaneous).
4th century CE *India*	Indian mathematicians work with place value and a base-10 system. Their numerals develop into the ones we use today, called the Hindu–Arabic numeral system.
7th century CE *India*	Brahmagupta discusses 0, the modern place value system, negative numbers, quadratic equations, and series.
c.820 CE *Persia*	Al-Khwarizmi writes a text which provides methods of solving equations and lays the foundation for modern algebra. He also popularises the Hindu–Arabic numeral system among Islamic mathematicians.
952 CE *Syria*	Al-Uqlidisi includes decimal fractions in the numeral system.
11th century CE *Persia*	Omar Khayyam writes about the triangle we now call Pascal's Triangle. He also solves cubic equations using geometric methods.
1202 CE *Italy*	Leonardo of Pisa (Fibonacci) introduces the Hindu–Arabic numeral system to Europe with his treatise *Liber Abaci*, which also contains the 'Fibonacci sequence'.
13th century CE *China*	Yang Hui writes about the triangle we now call Pascal's Triangle.
c. 1400 CE *Persia*	Al-Kashi writes extensively on decimal fractions.
1525 CE *Germany*	Christoff Rudolff publishes *Die Coss*, a textbook on algebra which introduces the radical sign, $\sqrt{}$, and the first instances of + and – in print.

Timeline of key mathematical events

1545 CE *Italy*	Gerolamo Cardano publishes the first examples of complex numbers and the method of solving cubic equations.
1570 CE *England*	Sir Henry Billingsley translates Euclid's *Elements* into English, choosing 'prime' for Euclid's *prōtos* – meaning 'first' – and establishing the word 'prime' as we now use it.
1572 CE *Italy*	Rafael Bombelli publishes *L'algebra*, which details how to solve cubic and quartic equations using complex numbers.
1585 CE *Netherlands*	Simon Stevin publishes *De Theinde*, which popularises decimal fractions in Europe, and *L'arithmétique*, which discusses solving general quadratic equations.
1610s CE *Scotland*	John Napier proposes logarithms in detail and invents 'Napier's Bones', numbered rods used for performing calculations.
1631 CE *England*	William Oughtred introduces the multiplication sign, $\times$. Later he introduces the slide rule and the abbreviations 'sin' and 'cos' in trigonometry.
1637 CE *France*	Pierre de Fermat writes his infamous claim about his last theorem in the margin of his copy of Diophantus' *Arithmetica*.
1637 CE *France*	René Descartes publishes *La Géométrie*, introducing the axes we now call the Cartesian grid. He is the first to use the phrase 'imaginary number' and describes the quadratic formula.
1659 CE *Switzerland*	Johann Rahn writes a textbook on algebra which includes the first instance of the obelus, $\div$, as the division sign.
1665 CE *France*	Blaise Pascal's *Traité du triangle arithmétique* is published, describing the triangle we now call Pascal's Triangle.
1684 CE *Germany*	Gottfried Wilhelm Leibniz publishes his first paper on calculus.
1687 CE *England*	Sir Isaac Newton develops his version of calculus and publishes *Principia Mathematica*, which contains the laws of motion and gravity that form the basis of classical mechanics.
1730s–40s CE *Russia and Germany*	Leonhard Euler introduces i for $\sqrt{(-1)}$ and the natural exponential e, and starts to consider transcendental numbers.
1743 CE *England*	William Emerson introduces the proportionality symbol, $\propto$.
1748 CE *Italy*	Maria Gaetana Agnesi writes one of the first comprehensive books on calculus.
1801 CE *Germany*	Carl Friedrich Gauss publishes *Disquisitiones Arithmeticae*, the first major work on modern number theory.
1874 CE *Germany*	Georg Cantor publishes work on the infinity of different sets of numbers.
1939–1947 CE *Russia and USA*	Mathematicians Kantorovich, Koopmans, Dantzig and von Neumann develop the optimisation process of linear programming based on inequalities in several variables.
1995 CE *England*	Sir Andrew Wiles publishes his proof of Fermat's Last Theorem.
2000 CE *USA*	The Clay Mathematics Institute proposes its seven Millennium Prize Problems.
2003 CE *Russia*	Grigori Perelman proves the Poincaré Conjecture, one of the Millennium Prize Problems.

Chapter 1

Number I: Representing and working with numbers

1.1 Number systems, place value and accuracy

> ✅ **Try this first**
>
> **1** Thinking about how our denary (**base** ten) number system works, explain how we would write the numbers 1 to 10 in base four (quaternary), with only the four digits 0, 1, 2 and 3 at our disposal.
>
> **2** When is 0.25 the same as 0.250?
>
> **3** Explain what happens to a number (in denary) when we multiply or divide by 10, 100, 1000, 0.1, 0.01, 0.001.

Place value and the workings of number underpin the whole of mathematics. Of course you know how numbers work, but in this section we are going to push your limits and see how robust your understanding really is.

Writing numbers

Throughout our history, humankind has developed different ways to record numbers. The method we use today is the denary, decimal or base ten system, and the symbols we use have taken a long journey from their inception in the Indian subcontinent around 1800 years ago, via Persian and Arabic mathematicians in the eighth century, until their introduction to Europe by Leonardo of Pisa, better known as Fibonacci, at the start of the thirteenth century (more in Section 4.1). It is generally considered that this system developed from counting with the ten digits on our hands or feet, but other cultures have used (and do use) different systems. The Mayans worked in a vigesimal (base twenty) system, the Babylonians in a sexagesimal (base sixty) system, and even today, in some areas of Nigeria and Nepal, a duodecimal (base twelve) system is used.

Getting to grips with the base system is really important for mathematics teachers and students, as it is this understanding that underpins all of our number work. How to round numbers, for instance, becomes obvious if we really understand how our numbers are formed.

A base system tells you how many digits you have at your disposal to record numbers. We have ten: 0, 1, 2, 3, 4, 5, 6, 7, 8, 9. Of themselves, these digits are just symbols. Put them together in various combinations and we create numerals, which are visual representations of the *idea* of a number. Each numeral has columns (which we introduce in the terms 'units' or 'ones', 'tens', 'hundreds', ... in primary school), and once we have exhausted all possible digits in a column we must introduce a new one. To make it clear which columns are being used, any empty columns are filled with **placeholder** zeros.

The same ten digits are used to represent parts of a whole – tenths, hundredths, thousandths, and so on – again with placeholders, and we can represent the names of the columns as powers of ten.

 Thinking about the classroom

As well as using the traditional column names, introduce your students to their associated powers of ten, both positive and negative, in a place value table. Early familiarity with these powers helps later work on **indices** and standard form.

A denary place value table for the number 7090.0456 might look like this.

10^3	10^2	10^1	10^0	.	10^{-1}	10^{-2}	10^{-3}	10^{-4}
thousands	hundreds	tens	units/ones	.	tenths	hundredths	thousandths	ten thousandths
7	0	9	0	.	0	4	5	6
This number can be expressed as $7\times10^3+0\times10^2+9\times10^1+0\times10^0+0\times10^{-1}+4\times10^{-2}+5\times10^{-3}+6\times10^{-4}$								

Working in other bases can reinforce and deepen understanding of base ten. In other bases we have a different number of digits at our disposal, like in this binary place value table, where we have only the digits 0 and 1.

2^3	2^2	2^1	2^0	.	2^{-1}	2^{-2}	2^{-3}	2^{-4}
eights	fours	twos	units/ones	.	halves	quarters	eighths	sixteenths
1	0	1	0	.	0	1	1	1
In denary, this number is $1\times2^3+0\times2^2+1\times2^1+0\times2^0+0\times2^{-1}+1\times2^{-2}+1\times2^{-3}+1\times2^{-4}=10.4375$								

Significance

So when is a zero *significant*? The difference between significant zeros and placeholders is one that is notoriously difficult for students to grasp. Take the number 0.005 06. There are four zero placeholders in that number – placeholders because without them the other digits would change value – but are they all significant? What about the number 24 070? Or 0.230?

The answer to the question is, 'it depends.' The first number you considered, 0.005 06, has the most straightforward answer. You know very little about that number until the first non-zero digit occurs, so the first three zeros are not significant, they are placeholders, whereas the zero between the 5 and the 6 *is* significant. Why do we count significant figures from the first non-zero digit? Because if we didn't we would end up approximating numbers as far apart as 0.4 and 0.000 000 000 000 000 001 to 0 (to one significant figure), which would be ridiculous! Having said that, don't be surprised when your students still try to count significant figures from the first digit, even once you've been through it.

For the other two examples, 24 070 and 0.230, you have to consider the purpose of a digit. This is best understood in the context of rounding. If the number 24 070 is exact, then all five digits are significant, including the placeholders. If it is the result of rounding, say, 24 069.5 to five significant figures (5 s.f.), then all five digits are significant. If, however, that number is the result of rounding, say, 24 072 to 4 s.f., then only the first four digits are significant and the final placeholder is not significant.

The third number, 0.230, is particularly interesting. The 0 at the end here is completely unnecessary in determining the **magnitude** of the number; it's equivalent to writing 056 instead of 56. But if that number is another number written to 3 s.f. (such as 0.2296 to 3 s.f.), then the 0 *is* significant; we are using it to denote the number's accuracy. In this case it is *not* a placeholder. This is a very difficult concept for many students, who are used to disregarding zeros at the end of a number after the decimal point.

 ## 1.1a Preparing to teach – do the mathematics!

Try these questions yourself before proceeding

You know how the base ten system works. Now transfer that understanding to another base system. Have a go at the following questions.

1 In base three (ternary), how many digits are at our disposal? What are they?

2 What is the value of the first column from the left of the decimal point in a number in base three? What about the second and third columns (to the left)? Or the nth column?

3 How would we write the numbers from one to ten in base three?

Moving digits

Now consider the third question from the introductory task: what happens when we multiply or divide any number by 10, 100, 1000, 0.1, 0.01, or 0.001? This may be so obvious to you that you are wondering why it needs to be considered, but did you answer by describing how the decimal point moves to the right or the left? If you did, then you are describing a common technique, but not what actually happens. The decimal point can't really move, but what *can* change is the place value of a digit. If we take 20 and divide it by 10, the digit '2' no longer represents 'two tens' but instead 'two units'; its value has decreased by a factor of ten. Similarly, if we take 78 and multiply it by 100, the digit '7' no longer represents 'seven tens' but instead 'seven thousands'; its value has increased by a factor of one hundred.

 Discuss

To what extent is it important to teach the change in the value of digits when multiplying and dividing by powers of 10? If the technique of moving the decimal point leads to the same answers should it be taught instead of, or in addition to, moving digits? What are the potential implications of telling students to move the decimal point?

Now consider what happens when you multiply a number by 0.1. This is the same as dividing by ten, since 0.1 represents one tenth; thinking in terms of 'one tenth (lots) of' can make the idea clearer. Conversely, we know that dividing by 0.1 is the same as multiplying by 10. The bar model in Figure 1.1 demonstrates this for the calculation $4 \div 0.1$. How does this model work?

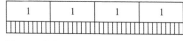

Figure 1.1

Students often have the misconception that multiplying makes a number bigger and dividing makes it smaller. Plenty of work is needed to get rid of this misconception. We will look at the multiplicative implications of numbers greater than 1, and those between 0 and 1, in more detail in Section 3.1.

 1.1b Preparing to teach – do the mathematics!

Try these questions yourself before proceeding

You are working in ternary (base three) again. What number do you multiply by to move all the digits one, two or three columns to the right or left?

1.2 Calculations and number theory

> ✓ **Try this first**
>
> **1** Why is it important to be able to write 24 as $2^3 \times 3$?
>
> **2** Explain the idea of 'borrowing' or 'exchanging' in column subtraction.
>
> **3** How can you tell if a number is divisible by 3? Why does this rule work?
>
> **4** What operations can replace the symbol * to make the **equation** true: $(2 * 3) * 6 = 2 * (3 * 6)$? Which ones would make it false? What property is demonstrated in this equation?

Fluency in the four operations is a cornerstone of developing mathematical understanding. Fluency in multiplication tables, for instance, enables students to more successfully do things like simplifying fractions or **factorising quadratics**, as they can concentrate their efforts on the new procedure or idea, rather than the numbers. Never underestimate the importance of fluency in calculation!

The importance of vocabulary

It is extremely important to introduce students to mathematical vocabulary at the earliest opportunity (see the Glossary pages of this book) and to make vocabulary building part of your teaching. With a shared, subject-specific vocabulary, you and your students will be able to make yourselves much better understood. Before we begin, here's some vocabulary you will know, and some you possibly won't.

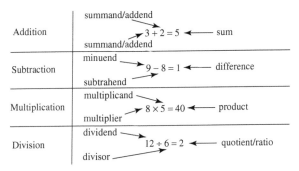

Addition	summand/addend $3 + 2 = 5$ ◄── sum summand/addend
Subtraction	minuend $9 - 8 = 1$ ◄── difference subtrahend
Multiplication	multiplicand $8 \times 5 = 40$ ◄── product multiplier
Division	dividend $12 \div 6 = 2$ ◄── quotient/ratio divisor

Figure 1.2

Common algorithms and why they work

How did you learn paper-and-pen calculations at school? Anyone over a certain age will have been taught the 'traditional' column algorithms, which many people still consider to be superior; others may have been taught multiplication using a grid. The debate rages on as to the 'best way' to multiply (as if a best way does actually exist in all cases), but there is certainly a general consensus that column algorithms are efficient. As a teacher you want to be sure of *how* those things you 'just know' actually work. Try these calculations and explain each step to yourself along the way. For the final division use long, rather than short, division.

$$
\begin{array}{cccc}
76 & 251 & 602 & \\
+359 & -86 & \times 214 & 24\overline{)9888}
\end{array}
$$

Let's consider the addition first. Where did you start? Why? What would happen if you started at the other end? (Try it, can you make it work?) Why do we 'carry the 1'? Explaining this comes down to place value: if you add two numbers together and the answer is at least ten, we need two columns to write the digits. More specifically, when you are adding the 7 and 5 and 1, you are really adding 70 and 50 and 10, so the 1 you 'carry over' represents one hundred and must go in the hundreds column.

Subtraction presents a little more conceptual difficulty. Why do we 'borrow' or 'exchange' 1 from the next column along when the **minuend** is smaller than the **subtrahend**? In our example, 1 − 6 would pose a problem, so we need to start from a larger number. We could start from 11, 21, 31 or more, but starting from 11 will result in a single-digit answer, which is required for the algorithm. The fact that we have used an extra 10 at the start to perform the initial subtraction means we mustn't use it a second time, and so we reduce the tens column by 1, hence the appearance of 'borrowing' or 'exchanging'. As an aside, can you make the subtraction work by borrowing 2 from the 5, instead of 1?

Moving on to multiplication: first, you multiply 602 by 4, carrying over numbers where necessary just as you do when adding. When you then multiply 602 by 1, you are in fact multiplying by 10, hence you must put a placeholder 0 in the units column. Similarly, as the 2 is in fact 200 we need two placeholder zeros.

Now for division. Long division is a process of repeated subtraction of the **divisor** from the **dividend**. At any point, you are working out how many complete divisors fit into a part of the dividend, subtracting this many of the divisors, then repeating the process with the remainder.

The column position of each digit is just as important in this algorithm as it is in the other three. When we say, 'how many 24s are in 98?' what we are really asking is 'how many 24s are in 9800?'. The answer is 400, so we write 4 above the first 8 in the hundreds column, and there are two implicit placeholder zeros over the next two 8s. Subtracting 9600 from 9888 leaves 288 and we repeat the process, 'how many 24s are in 288?'. It is worth noting here that short division works in exactly the same way as long division, only without writing out all the intermediate stages of subtraction underneath. Try the same calculation using short division to ensure you are convinced of this fact.

Some more multiplication

You will notice that the traditional algorithms are strict in their use of columnar position and place value, although this is not immediately obvious when executing them. For addition, subtraction and division, the column algorithms are practically ubiquitous in schools, whereas multiplication is often performed using one of two other methods. For the sake of thoroughness, let us consider how they work. First we have the grid, or box, method. We take 602×214 and split each number explicitly into hundreds, tens and units, using the grid to ensure every part of the multiplier is multiplied by every part of the **multiplicand**.

$\times$	600	2
200	120 000	400
10	6000	20
4	2400	8

Now **sum** the individual **products** in the grid to reach the final answer.

$120\,000 + 6000 + 2400 + 400 + 20 + 8 = 128\,828$

This method works on the principle of **distributivity** (discussed shortly):

$$\begin{aligned}
602 \times 214 &= (600 + 2) \times (200 + 10 + 4) \\
&= 600 \times (200 + 10 + 4) + 2 \times (200 + 10 + 4) \\
&= 600 \times 200 + 600 \times 10 + 600 \times 4 + 2 \times 200 + 2 \times 10 + 2 \times 4 \\
&= 120\,000 + 6000 + 2400 + 400 + 20 + 8
\end{aligned}$$

The second, slightly less common, form of multiplication is the lattice method, which is first evidenced in Arab writings from the late thirteenth century, an English paper from the turn of the fourteenth century and a

Chinese work from the mid-fifteenth century. It formed the basis of John Napier's 'bones', a device used for calculations with large numbers created by the Scottish Napier in the early seventeenth century and recommended by none other than Isaac Newton for its efficiency (examples can be seen in the Science Museum in London). The lattice method involves taking a grid and filling it in, as shown in Figure 1.3.

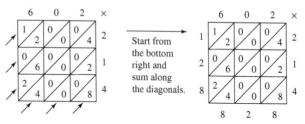

Figure 1.3

Reading from the top left, down, and then to the right, you can see the solution: 128828. This method is sometimes favoured as it avoids the potential of students missing off zeros, which is commonplace when using the standard grid method.

This method works in a similar way to the grid method, although you cannot see the placeholder zeros. Consider the number in the top right box, 04, which was created by multiplying 2 by 2. What you are actually multiplying is 2 by 200, so the digit 4 represents 400. If you consider every other digit in the diagonal containing this 4, each one displays the number of hundreds in the given calculation. By grouping digits that have the same value together in diagonals, the subsequent sums calculate the value of every column in the final answer.

All three of these algorithms are the same in their underlying structure, even though they look quite different in presentation. As with any mathematical process that has multiple approaches, it is worth taking a moment to consider *how* they are the same to ensure that your understanding of the procedures and why they work is robust.

 Discuss

What value is there in demonstrating more than one method of multiplication to students? Does learning multiple methods result in them being a master of none? Are some methods superior to others? Why?

Dealing with decimals

Adding and subtracting using the column algorithms is very straightforward with decimals, provided students line up the numbers correctly every time. When students are used to lining up their numbers from the right-hand side, then adding 24.56 and 139.2 can cause problems.

Multiplying and dividing with decimals can be much more problematic. To answer something like 12.4×1.36 it is much easier to begin with 124×136, using whichever algorithm you have chosen, and then to consider where the decimal point should go back into the answer. Since $124 \times 136 = 16\,864$ the decimal point is somewhere in the midst of these digits. It is not uncommon to hear teachers say something like 'there are three digits after the decimal points in the question (digits 4, 3 and 6) so there must be three digits after the decimal point in the answer, giving 16.864.' Why does this rule work?

The answer is to do with the adapted calculation we considered. 12.4 was multiplied by 10 to give 124, and 1.36 was multiplied by 100 to give 136. This means the whole calculation was multiplied by 1000 and the answer of 16 864 was 1000 times too big.

Another approach is to do an estimation. $12.4 \times 1.36 \approx 12 \times 1.5 \approx 18$. The only place the decimal point can go to make the number anywhere near 18 is 16.864. Of course, the accuracy of this approach depends on a student's estimation skills. Always be prepared for things that seem quite obvious to us to be anything but obvious to some of our students.

It is worth noting at this point that the lattice method deals with decimals in a lovely way, but one that isn't particularly clear to decipher. In the completed lattice in Figure 1.4, with decimal points intact, follow the arrows to see where the decimal point goes in the answer.

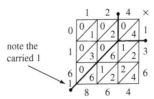

Figure 1.4

Take a moment now to think about why this works.

When dividing, **integer** divisors are much easier to work with than decimal ones. Take $7.62 \div 1.2$. If we write the division as $\dfrac{7.62}{1.2}$ and multiply the numerator and denominator by 10, then $\dfrac{76.2}{12}$ gives the same answer and is much easier to work with. You may find that students who do not understand why this process works will try to 'undo' their multiplying by 10 at the end, just as they do with multiplication; give them plenty of chances to see that both divisions give the same answer.

 Thinking about the classroom

The algorithms for the four operations require good understanding of two underlying elements: basic mental arithmetic, encompassing number bonds and times tables, and place value. Without good mental arithmetic, students will spend so much time and mental effort working with the numbers that they won't be able to focus on learning the algorithm. Without good understanding of place value, digits get lined up wrong, decimal points go in the wrong place, and students have no way of assessing whether or not their answer is feasible (which is the first step in spotting their own mistakes in mathematics).

Important properties of the four operations

Addition and multiplication have two particularly interesting properties: **commutativity** and **associativity**. They can seem a little obvious and, you might think, trivial, but they form a foundation of algebraic reasoning: understanding the concepts numerically helps when we generalise algebraically.

Addition and multiplication are commutative because $4 + 10 = 10 + 4$ or $2 \times 8 = 8 \times 2$. The numbers can be reversed, producing the same answer. The same cannot be said for subtraction or division, since $4 - 10 \neq 10 - 4$ and $12 \div 2 \neq 2 \div 12$. The commutativity of addition can be exploited to simplify seemingly complex calculations. Read the sum below from left to right.

$$12 + 91 + 72 + 61 + 28 + 39 + 88 + 9$$

It's not hard, but it's not exactly quick to solve. What if we utilise commutativity? We could write the calculation as:

$$12 + 88 + 91 + 9 + 72 + 28 + 61 + 39$$

Now it's clear that successive pairs of numbers sum to 100 and the answer is 400.

Addition and multiplication are associative because $(5 + 3) + 2 = 5 + (3 + 2)$

or $(6 \times 1) \times 8 = 6 \times (1 \times 8)$. It does not matter in which order the operations are performed (although the sequence is not reversed, in the way that it is in commutativity). Associativity is demonstrated beautifully in examples such as this, where a **multiple** of 8 is dissociated from the multiplier and associated with the multiplicand:

$$48 \times 0.125 = (6 \times 8) \times 0.125 = 6 \times (8 \times 0.125) = 6 \times 1 = 6$$

A third property, called **distributivity,** can be demonstrated with the example:

$$6 \times 24 = 6 \times (20 + 4) = 6 \times 20 + 6 \times 4$$

Multiplication distributes over addition and subtraction, as does division. You use distributivity all the time, possibly without realising it. (If I asked you to work out 6×24 you probably would have done it the way shown above, without considering it so formally.)

Getting to grips with these properties when working with number provides an important starting point for understanding algebraic reasoning, and increases the strategies available for mental arithmetic. What you will find is that students who can happily distribute multiplication are not so sure when it comes to division. Consider the calculation:

$$\frac{354}{3} = \frac{300 + 30 + 24}{3} = \frac{300}{3} + \frac{30}{3} + \frac{24}{3} = 100 + 10 + 8 = 118$$

Most students will be less confident with this mental process than they are with the process for 6×24 above. This lack of confidence translates to algebra, when it is not clear that $\frac{4x^2 + 6x}{2x}$ can be simplified by dividing each term in the numerator by the $2x$ in the denominator. Spend time allowing students to not only develop arithmetic fluencies but to articulate them as well. This will be invaluable when it comes to algebra later on.

Another important pair of properties to be able to identify are the **inverse** and **identity** of addition and multiplication. An inverse undoes an operation, so the **additive inverse** of a is $-a$, and the **multiplicative inverse** of a is $\frac{1}{a}$. An identity does not change a number, hence the **additive identity** is 0 and the **multiplicative identity** is 1. Note the relationship between identities and inverses:

number + additive inverse = additive identity e.g. $2 + (-2) = 0$

number $\times$ multiplicative inverse = multiplicative identity e.g. $2 \times \frac{1}{2} = 1$

Further exploration

The properties of identity and inverse take on even greater significance in more advanced mathematics. For instance, advanced mathematics students will study matrices and **functions**, for which the concepts of the identity matrix and inverse function are pivotal. So it may seem that these ideas are trivial and not worth understanding but, as with everything in mathematics, they can be extended to great depth.

Negative numbers

Negative numbers can be a sticking point for some students, with commonly used phrases causing all sorts of problems. Phrases like 'two minuses make a plus' often end up with a student saying that $-7 + -3$ equals 10, or even 4. The idea of negative numbers being 'smaller' than positive numbers is a misleading one. Is -5 smaller than 0.5? It is certainly 'less than', but does 'less than' mean 'smaller'?

The **absolute value**, or magnitude, of a number is its size, regardless of its sign, and we signify the absolute value using straight lines around a number, so $|-5| = 5$. This means the absolute value of -5 is the same as the absolute value of 5. They have the same size, they just go in different directions from 0. It makes sense to think about -10 being 'more negative' than, say, -3 (and 'less than' is absolutely correct, too) but 'smaller than' is misleading, since -0.01 is definitely a smaller number than -1.

Look at Figure 1.5. Thinking about the number line as going in two directions from 0, as if there is a line of reflection through 0, can help to conceptualise operations with negative numbers, and how they relate to operations with positive numbers.

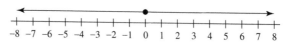

Figure 1.5

In Figure 1.6, we can see that $4 + 3$ has an equivalent calculation in the other direction, $-4 + -3$, and where the first has answer 7, the second has answer -7. Similarly with subtraction, if $6 - 4 = 2$, then $-6 - -4 = -2$.

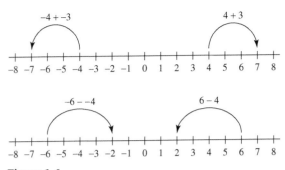

Figure 1.6

By starting with calculations like these, students have the chance to become familiar with the following ideas: adding a positive number moves right on the number line, whereas adding a negative moves left; subtracting a positive moves left on the number line, whereas subtracting a negative moves right. (If you use a vertical number line the same ideas still hold, but with up and down.) If the number you are adding or subtracting is negative, it reverses the 'normal' direction of movement, the one students have always known to that point. Helping students to identify, in each calculation, which is the starting number, what direction they are moving in, and then how many steps to move will stop them arbitrarily trying to apply rules like 'two minuses make a plus'.

 Discuss

Some people like to teach negative numbers using a horizontal line, since students are familiar with this from primary school. Other people prefer a vertical line, often because of its links with concrete objects such as thermometers. Should all students in your department be taught in the same way? Should they encounter both representations regularly or is one sufficient? Should teachers display a permanent number line in the classroom or does this stop students from having to think for themselves?

We will return to negative numbers and the concept of the number line going in two directions from 0 in Section 3.1, when we look at multiplication and division.

Order of operations

The agreed order of operations has developed over time. Even as recently as the early 1900s, mathematicians were arguing over whether multiplication or division should take precedence, but sometime in the twentieth century everything settled down to what we accept as convention now.

The order in which operations must be performed – anything in brackets (including implied brackets, such as the fraction bar in $\frac{3+5}{2}$), indices (including roots), multiplication/division, addition/subtraction – has layers of complexity that need to be addressed in the classroom. Sometimes students learn mnemonics such as BIDMAS or PEMDAS (where the P is 'parentheses' and the E is '**exponents**') and rigidly stick to the order of the letters. However, this can lead to mistakes. Take $3 \times 4 \div 2 \times 9 \div 2$. A student strictly following PEMDAS will do multiplication before division and will end up calculating $12 \div 18 \div 2$, which is incorrect. In $3 - 4 + 2 - 9 + 2$, a student strictly following BIDMAS would end up with $3 - 6 - 11$, doing addition before subtraction, which is again incorrect. Division and multiplication have equal priority and should be worked from left to right, as should addition and subtraction. To get around this some teachers propose using a pyramid like the one shown in Figure 1.7.

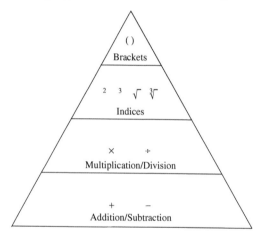

Figure 1.7

The mnemonics are not bad in themselves but can be used poorly. It is important to remember that the mnemonic is not the mathematics, it is only an aid to teaching something properly. It is often best to leave the mnemonics (or any *aide-memoire*) until the mathematics has been taught.

Spend time on the left–right reading of division/multiplication and addition/subtraction before you even think about introducing the other operations. What many students fail to appreciate, even after being taught the order of operations, is that left–right multiplication and division can actually be reordered, and the reordering made clearer if you make use of a fraction bar. Take $3 \times 4 \div 2 \times 9 \div 2$. In this calculation, the number 3 is multiplied by 4 and 9 and also divided by 2 and 2. This could be rewritten as $\frac{3 \times 4 \times 9}{2 \times 2} = \frac{108}{4} = 27$.

Grouping the divisors separately from the multipliers can make some calculations easier. The same principle can be applied to left–right addition and subtraction, where we can group **summands** and subtrahends:

$$5 - 7 + 12 - 15 + 20 - 1 = (5 + 12 + 20) - (7 + 15 + 1) = 37 - 23 = 14$$

Students who are confident in going from $5 - 7 + 12 - 15 + 20 - 1$ straight to $37 - 23$, or from $3 \times 4 \div 2 \times 9 \div 2$ to $108 \div 4$, will be much more fluent in calculation and will have a greater number sense, which is later transferable to algebra.

 Thinking about the classroom

Students are more likely to remember what they spend the most time on and think about the most. With this in mind, don't start a mathematical topic with a mnemonic or an *aide-memoire*, as students will end up remembering this more than the mathematics. Order of operations is a perfect example. Many misconceptions or common mistakes can be avoided by helping students to understand the left–right nature of multiplication/division and addition/subtraction, and then explaining where they fit in the hierarchy of all operations, before even thinking about bringing in something like BIDMAS. You might even find you don't need the mnemonic if you do this.

 1.2a Preparing to teach – do the mathematics!

Try these questions yourself before proceeding

 Which properties or special features of the four operations are demonstrated in the following calculations?

   a. $3 \times 6 = 6 \times 3$

   b. $\frac{1}{8} \times 8 = 1$

   c. $37.5 \times 8 = 3 \times 12.5 \times 8 = 3 \times 100 = 300$

   d. $5 - 2 + 4 + 2 = 5 + 4 - 2 + 2 = 5 + 4 = 9$

   e. $38 \times 7 = 40 \times 7 - 2 \times 7 = 280 - 14 = 266$

 What is the answer to the calculation $-2 \div 4(3 + -1)$?

Factors, multiples and primes

Prime numbers are the building blocks of all the **natural numbers** and have important applications in computing, especially in public-key cryptography and internet security. In the school curriculum, a clear understanding of **factors**, multiples and primes feeds into a range of further topics, including fractions and algebraic manipulation. The concepts of the lowest common multiple (LCM) and highest common factor (HCF) are essential in this. How might you find the LCM of 24 and 30? Perhaps the most straightforward and direct way is to list the multiples of both numbers until you reach the first common multiple, as shown below.

Multiples of 24: 24, 48, 72, 96, **120**, ...

Multiples of 30: 30, 60, 90, **120**, ...

LCM(24, 30) = 120

In a similar way, we can find the HCF of two numbers, say, 60 and 72:

Factors of 60: 1, 2, 3, 4, 5, 6, 10, **12**, 15, 20, 30, 60

Factors of 72: 1, 2, 3, 4, 6, 8, 9, **12**, 18, 24, 36, 72

HCF(60, 72) = 12

Listing is rather like a brute force attack: not very elegant and quite inefficient as the numbers in question get larger, especially with infinite lists of multiples. As is the way with mathematics, however, there is a better approach, and it involves the fundamental **theorem** of arithmetic.

The fundamental theorem of arithmetic states that every integer greater than 1 is either prime or can be expressed as a unique product of prime factors (numbers that are not prime are **composite**). In practice, you are expressing a number in terms of its building blocks and no matter how you search for those blocks, you will always end up at the same unique factorisation (see below). Figure 1.8 shows two different ways of breaking down the number 12. Either way, $12 = 2 \times 2 \times 3$.

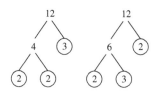

Figure 1.8

Using the theorem it becomes clear why 1 is not considered a prime number. If it were, then there would not be a single factorisation for each number but rather an infinite number of factorisations. For instance, you could have $12 = 2^2 \times 3 = 2^2 \times 3 \times 1 = 2^2 \times 3 \times 1 \times 1 = \ldots$. So, by definition, 1 is not a prime number, since a prime number must have exactly two *distinct* factors: itself and 1.

If you know the prime factorisation of two numbers, these building blocks can be used to find the HCF and the LCM. The HCF is quite intuitive: a common factor of 60 and 72 must be a number that is itself built of factors of 60 and 72. For instance, 2 and 3 are factors of 60 and of 72, so their product, 6, must also be a factor of 60 and 72. It then follows that if you identify *all* the shared prime factors of 60 and 72, their product must be the highest common factor. See Figure 1.9 for an illustration that HCF(60, 72) = $2 \times 2 \times 3 = 12$.

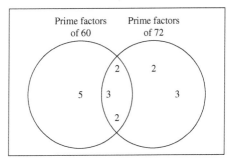

Figure 1.9

If two numbers have no common factors (apart from 1), then we say they are **coprime**. Any fraction that cannot be simplified is one where the numerator and denominator are coprime.

Now let's use prime factors to find the LCM of 24 and 30. Their prime factor decompositions are $2^3 \times 3$ and $2 \times 3 \times 5$, respectively. A Venn diagram containing the prime factors is shown in Figure 1.10.

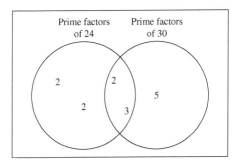

Figure 1.10

The intersection on the Venn diagram represents the prime factors that make the HCF of 24 and 30, namely, 6. First we multiply 6 by the two unused factors that made 24 (2 and 2), then by the unused factor that made 30 (5). Our result is the number that is simultaneously the smallest possible multiple of both 24 and 30 (Figure 1.11).

39

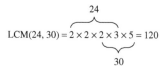

$$LCM(24, 30) = 2 \times 2 \times 2 \times 3 \times 5 = 120$$

Figure 1.11

One fascinating use of prime factors is in analysing numbers. For instance, we can use them to find the square root of a number.

$$275\,625 = 3^2 \times 5^4 \times 7^2 = (3 \times 5^2 \times 7)^2 = 525^2 \therefore \sqrt{275\,625} = 525$$

We can also use them to find all factors of a number. Let's say we wish to know all the factors of 504. If we start from the fact that $504 = 2^3 \times 3^2 \times 7$, then we can use some systematic listing to find all the factors of 504 by multiplying together different combinations of its prime factors. Let's begin with a list of all the prime factors and find all possible distinct combinations of them.

Pairs	Triples
2×2; 2×3; 2×7; 3×3; 3×7	$2 \times 3 \times 7$; $2 \times 2 \times 2$; $2 \times 2 \times 3$; $2 \times 2 \times 7$; $3 \times 3 \times 2$; $3 \times 3 \times 7$
Quadruples	**Quintuples**
$2 \times 3 \times 3 \times 7$; $2 \times 2 \times 2 \times 3$; $2 \times 2 \times 2 \times 7$; $2 \times 2 \times 3 \times 3$; $2 \times 2 \times 3 \times 7$	$2 \times 2 \times 2 \times 3 \times 3$; $2 \times 2 \times 2 \times 3 \times 7$; $2 \times 2 \times 3 \times 3 \times 7$

So we have all the factors of 504 (including 1, 504 and each of the single-digit prime factors):

1, 2, 3, 4, 6, 7, 8, 9, 12, 14, 18, 21, 24, 28, 36, 42, 56, 63, 72, 84, 126, 168, 252, 504

 1.2b Preparing to teach – do the mathematics!

Try these questions yourself before proceeding

Using prime factors, show the following results.

1 The product of two numbers is equal to the product of their HCF and LCM.

2 The smallest perfect square divisible by 24, 36 and 84 is 7056.

Thinking about the classroom

Students are forever mixing up factors and multiples, and you will soon realise that when they don't quite know the difference between a factor and a multiple, then the phrases 'highest common factor' and 'lowest common multiple' make little sense. Spend more time than you initially think you will need on the difference between these two terms.

While we're considering primes, we need to mention their infinity. Euclid, the Greek mathematician from the third century BCE, whose book, *Elements*, is quite probably the most influential text in the history of mathematics and earned its author the moniker 'the father of geometry', was the first to record that the primes are infinite. His *proof* is elegant and begins by assuming that the primes are finite. List all the primes (which is possible because they are finite) and multiply them together. Now add 1 to the answer. This new number must be either prime or composite (since every integer greater than 1 is either prime or composite). Now consider these two scenarios.

1 If this new number is prime, then our list of 'all primes' was incomplete.

2 If this new number is composite, then it must be divisible by a prime number. The problem is that, before we added 1, we had a number that was divisible by every prime on our list. Then we added 1, and since 1 is not divisible by any prime, then our new number is not divisible by any prime on the list. If our new number is composite, our list must have been missing a prime number.

Either way, our list of 'all primes' was incomplete. Since this can be repeated with any list of primes it is impossible to list them all, so the primes must be infinite.

 Further exploration

The mathematics surrounding the prime numbers is a goldmine. We know they are infinite, but we don't have a way of predicting the next prime. We do, however, have estimates for the number of primes less than a certain number (this is called the prime number theorem). We know there are infinitely many primes and there are several proofs of this (in addition to Euclid's, which we've already mentioned) that are well worth a read. Euclid also produced an algorithm for finding the HCF of two numbers, which he described geometrically in terms of the lengths of lines in *Elements*.

One of the greatest unsolved problems in mathematics is the proof of the Riemann hypothesis, named after German mathematician Bernhard Riemann, who did extensive work on prime numbers in the nineteenth century and whose hypothesis reveals much about the distribution of prime numbers. The Clay Mathematics Institute (New Hampshire, USA) has a prize of £1 million for the person who proves this problem, and a handful of others (more on this in Section 4.3).

Divisibility rules

We all know that an even number is divisible by 2 and a number that ends in 5 or 0 is divisible by 5. Many people know that if the digital sum (sum of all the digits) of a number is divisible by 3, then so is the number itself. How do we know if a number is divisible by 4, 6, 7, 8, 9 or 11? Take a moment to note down which of these divisibility rules you know.

While we take a look at them, bear in mind that some numbers have multiple rules, but we will consider only one rule for each here.

Divisor	Divisibility rule
1	All integers are divisible by 1.
2	The last digit is even/divisible by 2.
3	The digital sum is divisible by 3.
4	The last two digits are themselves a number divisible by 4.
5	The last digit is 5 or 0.
6	The number is divisible by both 2 and 3 (see the rules for 2 and 3).
7	Group the digits in threes, starting from the end. Successively subtract and add each group until all digits are used up. If the answer is divisible by 7, so was the original number. This can be repeated until the answer is clear.
8	The last three digits are themselves a number divisible by 8.
9	The digital sum is divisible by 9.
10	The last digit is 0.
11	Starting from the first digit, alternately subtract and add the subsequent digits. If the answer is divisible by 11, so was the original number.

As with everything, we must ask *why* these rules work so that we have the depth of understanding required of someone trying to teach others well. In order to understand these rules you need to use the fact that, for any number, n, with k digits each of the form a_i:

$$n = \sum_{i=1}^{k} 10^{i-1} a_i = 10^0 a_1 + 10^1 a_2 + 10^2 a_3 + \ldots + 10^{k-1} a_k$$

Don't be put off by the notation here. This is a beautifully concise way of saying that any number can be written as the sum of its last digit, its second-to-last digit multiplied by 10, its third-to-last digit multiplied by 100, and so on. So a two-digit number, $a_2 a_1$, can be written $10^1 a_2 + 10^0 a_1$ (such as $23 = 10 \times 2 + 1 \times 3$), or a four-digit number, $a_4 a_3 a_2 a_1$, can be written $10^3 a_4 + 10^2 a_3 + 10^1 a_2 + 10^0 a_1$ (such as $9235 = 1000 \times 9 + 100 \times 2 + 10 \times 3 + 1 \times 5$). This is the same representation of a number as we saw in the place value table in Section 1.1.

Now, take any number, n. For now, let's assume n is five digits, of the form $abcde$, then we have:

$$n = 10^4 a + 10^3 b + 10^2 c + 10d + e$$
$$= 10\,000a + 1000b + 100c + 10d + e$$
$$= 2(5000a + 500b + 50c + 5d) + e$$

A factor of 2 has been taken out of the first four terms, and could be taken out of the last term only if this number is divisible by 2. Hence, n is divisible by 2 if and only if its last digit is divisible by 2. Since all numbers can be written in the same way, this is true for all numbers, no matter their size.

Let's apply the same process to demonstrate the divisibility rule for 9, using the same five-digit number.

$$n = 10^4 a + 10^3 b + 10^2 c + 10d + e$$
$$= 10\,000a + 1000b + 100c + 10d + e$$
$$= (9999 + 1)a + (999 + 1)b + (99 + 1)c + (9 + 1)d + e$$
$$= 9999a + 999b + 99c + 9d + a + b + c + d + e$$
$$= 9(1111a + 111b + 11c + d) + a + b + c + d + e$$

You will notice here that we used distributivity in the third line and commutativity in the fourth line. If the sum $a + b + c + d + e$ is divisible by 9, then a factor of 9 can be taken from the entire expression, and the number n is divisible by 9. Since any power of ten is equal to one more than a multiple of 9, any number is equal to a multiple of 9 plus the sum of its digits, as per the demonstration above. Therefore, any number is divisible by 9 if and only if the sum of its digits is divisible by 9.

Again, using our five-digit number, n, let's consider divisibility by 4.

$$n = 10^4 a + 10^3 b + 10^2 c + 10d + e$$
$$= 4(2500a + 250b + 25c) + 10d + e$$

Since $10d + e$ represents a two-digit number formed from the last two digits of n, then if this two-digit number is divisible by 4, so is n. As above, this can be generalised to any number, not just those with five digits.

1.2c Preparing to teach – do the mathematics!

Try these questions yourself before proceeding

1 Using the ideas introduced, prove the divisibility rules for 10, 5, 3 and 8.

2 Thinking about factors, what is the simplest way to prove the divisibility rule for 6?

3 Which single-digit numbers is 378 000 divisible by?

Now onto the toughest two. Starting with 7, let's reuse our five-digit n and introduce the useful but obscure fact that $1000 = 7 \times 143 - 1$.

$$n = 10^4 a + 10^3 b + 10^2 c + 10d + e$$
$$= 1000(10a + b) + 100c + 10d + e$$
$$= (7 \times 143 - 1)(10a + b) + 100c + 10d + e$$
$$= 7 \times 143(10a + b) - (10a + b) + 100c + 10d + e$$

This will be divisible by 7 if $100c + 10d + e - (10a + b)$ is divisible by 7. This expression represents taking the number formed by the last three digits and subtracting the number formed by the next two.

To apply this rule to a number with more than five digits we must group the number into three digit multiples and use the fact that any power of 1000 differs from a multiple of 7 by 1.

$1000 = 7 \times 143 - 1$,

$1000^2 = 7 \times 142\,857 + 1$,

$1000^3 = 7 \times 142\,857\,143 - 1$, ...

The fact that these powers of 1000 alternate between being 1 less than and 1 more than a multiple of 7 results in the alternating addition and subtraction that is necessary. Beginning with the number formed by the end three digits we subtract the number formed by the next three, add the number formed by the next three, and so on.

Finally, the rule for divisibility by 11 is demonstrated in a similar way to that of 7, using:

$10 = 11 - 1$,

$100 = 9 \times 11 + 1$,

$1000 = 91 \times 11 - 1$,

$10\,000 = 909 \times 11 + 1$, ...

That is, each power of ten differs from a multiple of 11 by 1. Reusing our five-digit n for one last time:

$$n = 10^4 a + 10^3 b + 10^2 c + 10d + e$$
$$= (909 \times 11 + 1)a + (91 \times 11 - 1)b + (9 \times 11 + 1)c + (11 - 1)d + e$$
$$= 909 \times 11a + a + 91 \times 11b - b + 9 \times 11c + c + 11d - d + e$$
$$= 11 \times 909a + 11 \times 91b + 11 \times 9c + 11d + a - b + c - d + e$$
$$= 11(909a + 91b + 9c + d) + a - b + c - d + e$$

If the alternating sum $a - b + c - d + e$ is divisible by 11, then so is the original number, n. As with all these demonstrations, it holds for a number of any size.

> ### Further exploration
>
> If you would like to explore these (and other) divisibility proofs further, read up on *modular arithmetic*, which makes our explanations here much more concise and elegant.

1.3 Rational and irrational numbers

> ### ✓ Try this first
>
> **1** Which fractions produce recurring decimals and which produce terminating decimals? How do you know?
>
> **2** Which of the following roots are integers?
>
> $\sqrt{40}, \ \sqrt{400}, \ \sqrt{4000}, \ \sqrt{40\,000}$
>
> How can you show this without calculating the roots directly?
>
> **3** What is the value of $\left(\dfrac{125}{27}\right)^{-\frac{2}{3}}$?
>
> **4** How is $\dfrac{\sqrt{2}}{2}$ equivalent to $\dfrac{1}{\sqrt{2}}$? Why is writing $\dfrac{\sqrt{2}}{2}$ preferable to writing $\dfrac{1}{\sqrt{2}}$?

Parts of a whole

We have two main ways, in the decimal system, of representing parts of a whole: fractions and decimals. Both of these are actually fractions, and the stricter terminology for each is *vulgar fractions* and *decimal fractions*. The word 'fraction' comes from the Latin *fractio*, meaning 'breaking' (in the religious sense of breaking bread), so a fraction is a number that breaks a whole into parts. The word 'vulgar' comes from the Latin *vulgus*, meaning 'common people' or 'the masses', and was in use years ago to represent fractions used in ordinary calculations, or used commonly. Thus, a vulgar fraction is any fraction expressed with a numerator and a denominator.

You can contrast this with a decimal fraction – a fraction that breaks a whole into decimal (base 10) parts, which is exactly what a number such as 0.905 does, being 905 thousandths. Decimal fractions were first proposed in Europe by the Flemish mathematician Simon Stevin in his book *De Theinde* ('The Tenth') in 1585, although they can be found in Arab and Chinese works as far back as the tenth century. Stevin suggests that a decimal system be used for measuring and coinage, but it took a good few centuries before his suggestion really caught on.

A decimal as we know it is just another way of writing a vulgar fraction that has a power of ten in the denominator. Of course, in modern usage we almost always mean 'vulgar fraction' when we say 'fraction', and we could probably more accurately call what we know as a 'decimal' a 'decimal expansion of a decimal fraction', although this is an unnecessary mouthful!

The wording here becomes sticky when we consider recurring decimals. A number such as $0.\dot{3}$ has an infinite decimal expansion, and as a vulgar fraction is $\frac{1}{3}$. Its denominator is not a power of 10, and cannot be written as a power of 10. The word 'decimal' appears to be the wrong kind of word to use here. Fortunately, language is not always a pedant.

Recurring decimals introduce some very interesting ideas. Think about the following argument.

$$\text{If } \frac{1}{3} = 0.\dot{3}, \text{ then } \frac{2}{3} = 0.\dot{6} \text{ and } \frac{3}{3} = 0.\dot{9}. \text{ But } \frac{3}{3} = 1, \text{ so } 0.\dot{9} = 1.$$

That blows the minds of most students (and many adults)! We can show that $0.\dot{9} = 1$ in a number of other ways, of varying degrees of accessibility to students. The following table shows three such ways.

Alternative 1	Alternative 2	Alternative 3
Let $x = 0.\dot{9}$ then $10x = 9.\dot{9}$ and $10x - x = 9x = 9$. So $x = \dfrac{9}{9} = 1$.	$1 - 0.1 = 0.9$ $1 - 0.01 = 0.99$ $1 - 0.001 = 0.999$ $1 - 0.0001 = 0.9999$ ... $1 - 0.0000... = 0.9999...$	Using the calculation to find the midpoint of two numbers, find the midpoint of $\dfrac{1}{3}$ and $\dfrac{2}{3}$.
	So, to get from 1 to $0.\dot{9}$ we must subtract $0.\dot{0}$, which is 0.	$\dfrac{\frac{1}{3} + \frac{2}{3}}{2} = \dfrac{0.\dot{3} + 0.\dot{6}}{2}$ $\dfrac{\frac{3}{3}}{2} = \dfrac{0.\dot{9}}{2}$ $\dfrac{1}{2} = \dfrac{0.\dot{9}}{2}$ This can be true only if $0.\dot{9} = 1$.

The equivalence of $0.\dot{9}$ and 1 demonstrates that every (non-zero) terminating decimal has, in fact, two equivalent decimal expansions, so the number 9.31 could also be written $9.30\dot{9}$ and the number 0.45 could also be written $0.44\dot{9}$. The choice of which to use comes down to efficiency and clarity.

Terminating vs. recurring

How do we know if a fraction will produce a terminating or recurring decimal? What about $\dfrac{4}{5}$ or $\dfrac{5}{9}$? How about $\dfrac{12}{30}$ or $\dfrac{13}{30}$? It all comes down to the denominator. A fraction can only produce a terminating decimal if, when in its simplest form, its denominator has only 2s or 5s for prime factors.

Why is this? We know that any terminating decimal can be written as a fraction with a denominator that is a power of 10, so we have $0.3 = \dfrac{3}{10}$ or $0.58 = \dfrac{58}{100} = \dfrac{29}{50}$. Since the prime factor decomposition of 10 is 2×5, the prime factor decomposition of any power of 10 is a power of 2×5 ($100 = 10^2 = 2^2 \times 5^2$, $100\,000 = 10^5 = 2^5 \times 5^5$, $10^n = 2^n \times 5^n$). This means that the denominator of a fraction must be composed of only 2s and 5s if we are to be able to write it as a power of 2×5.

For instance, $\dfrac{5}{8} = \dfrac{5}{2^3}$, which can be turned into $\dfrac{625}{1000}$ by multiplying numerator and denominator by 5^3. However, $\dfrac{4}{15} = \dfrac{4}{3 \times 5}$, so we cannot make the denominator a power of 10 and it must produce a recurring decimal.

 Thinking about the classroom

Students often fail to associate the fraction bar with division. The idea that $\dfrac{5}{6}$ represents the same value as $5 \div 6$ and can be converted to decimal form by performing this division is something that seems to slip from memory quickly. This can be helped by regularly writing division calculations with a fraction bar and not shying away from leaving answers to divisions in fraction form (including when solving equations).

 1.3a Preparing to teach – do the mathematics!

Try these questions yourself before proceeding

1 If the number $\dfrac{3}{13}$ is written as a decimal, find the thirtieth digit after the decimal point.

2 The repetend of a recurring decimal is its repeating digits. For instance, $\dfrac{25}{99} = 0.\overset{\cdot}{2}\overset{\cdot}{5}$, with repetend 25.

    a. How long is the repetend of $\dfrac{1}{9}, \dfrac{1}{99}, \dfrac{1}{999}$, etc?

    b. How long is the repetend of the following numbers and how does this length relate to your answer to part (a): $\dfrac{1}{3}, \dfrac{1}{7}, \dfrac{1}{11}, \dfrac{1}{13}$?

Calculations with fractions

Many mathematicians would argue that fractions are superior to decimals. Fractions represent not just the exact value of a solution (whereas decimals bring the temptation to round), but convey the **proportional** relationship involved in the number in question. It is arguably easier to conceptualise $\dfrac{13}{1000}$ than 0.013. Fluency with fraction calculations gives the added benefit of greater precision when working with **irrational** numbers such as $\dfrac{\sqrt{2}}{2}$, where decimals quickly bring in inaccuracy; this fluency can be achieved with much more regular exposure to these calculations than many students receive – a stand-alone unit will not do the job.

Visual representations help us to understand why these calculations work: a fraction wall makes clear the need for a common denominator when adding and subtracting, for instance. The fraction wall in Figure 1.12 illustrates $\frac{1}{3} + \frac{1}{4}$.

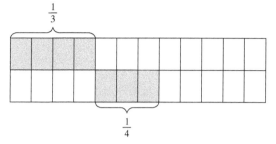

Figure 1.12

Images for multiplying and dividing fractions need a little more thought. In the case of multiplying, an image doesn't necessarily make the algorithm easier to understand (it is, after all, the most straightforward of all the fraction calculations) but it does provide an interesting aside. Figure 1.13 links to the idea of multiplication as a rectangular array, a theme which recurs even into algebraic multiplication, and illustrates $\frac{5}{8} \times \frac{2}{3}$. The shaded overlap shows $\frac{5}{8}$ of $\frac{2}{3}$, or $\frac{5}{8} \times \frac{2}{3}$.

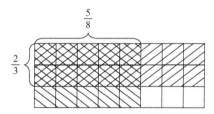

Figure 1.13

It is also important, when multiplying, to get the hang of simplifying the calculation first, so that instead of something like $\frac{4}{9} \times \frac{2}{5} \times \frac{15}{8} \times \frac{3}{2} = \frac{360}{720} = \frac{1}{2}$, we have:

$$\frac{{}^{1}\cancel{4}}{{}_{,\cancel{3}}\cancel{9}} \times \frac{{}^{1}\cancel{2}}{{}_{1}\cancel{5}} \times \frac{{}^{1\cancel{3}}\cancel{15}}{{}_{2}\cancel{8}} \times \frac{{}^{1}\cancel{3}}{{}_{1}\cancel{2}} = \frac{1}{2}$$

This works by commutativity, simplifying the fractions $\frac{4}{8}$, $\frac{2}{2}$, $\frac{15}{5}$ and $\frac{3}{9}$, then the $\frac{3}{3}$ that appears after this first lot of simplification.

Since division is the inverse of multiplication, the same algorithm works for both, so we can divide in the numerator and divide in the denominator.

$$\frac{9}{16} \div \frac{3}{4} = \frac{9 \div 3}{16 \div 4} = \frac{3}{4}$$

Problems arise, however, when these individual divisions don't produce integers:

$$\frac{9}{16} \div \frac{5}{7} = \frac{9 \div 5}{16 \div 7} = \frac{\frac{9}{5}}{\frac{16}{7}}$$

We can use what we know about equivalent fractions to tidy up this answer. When we say that $\frac{1}{2}$ is equivalent to $\frac{2}{4}$ we are multiplying $\frac{1}{2}$ by $\frac{2}{2}$, which is, of course, 1, and multiplying by 1 doesn't change a number; it's the multiplicative identity. Let's multiply our answer above by $\frac{5}{5}$.

$$\frac{\frac{9}{5}}{\frac{16}{7}} \times \frac{5}{5} = \frac{9}{\frac{80}{7}}$$

Now let's multiply it by $\frac{7}{7}$.

$$\frac{9}{\frac{80}{7}} \times \frac{7}{7} = \frac{63}{80}$$

By writing these successive multiplications in one go you can see where the standard algorithm of changing the division to multiplication and reciprocating the second fraction comes from.

$$\frac{9}{16} \div \frac{5}{7} = \frac{\frac{9}{\cancel{5}}}{\frac{16}{\cancel{7}}} \times \frac{\cancel{5}}{5} \times \frac{7}{\cancel{7}} = \frac{9}{16} \times \frac{7}{5} = \frac{63}{80}$$

Division of fractions, and the idea behind the algorithm, can be conceptualised with a bar model, remembering the idea of division as 'how many times does a go into b?'. The bar in Figure 1.14 shows that $3 \div \frac{1}{2} = 6$.

1		1		1	
$\frac{1}{2}$	$\frac{1}{2}$	$\frac{1}{2}$	$\frac{1}{2}$	$\frac{1}{2}$	$\frac{1}{2}$

Figure 1.14

The image is much more complex, and probably muddies the waters, when we don't have an integer dividend, as you can see in the bar model of $\frac{2}{5} \div \frac{1}{2}$ in Figure 1.15.

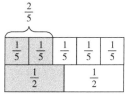

Figure 1.15

We can see that less than $\frac{1}{2}$ fits into $\frac{2}{5}$, but it is not clear what fraction of $\frac{1}{2}$ does the job. Images provide a 'way in' to many ideas, but there comes a point where a mathematical process goes beyond the capabilities of an image.

 Thinking about the classroom

A bar model like those in Figures 1.14 and 1.15 can be very useful in many areas of mathematics, from ratio to equations, and especially fractions. We can use them to convert improper fractions to mixed numbers, as well as to represent the four operations. By using one visualisation such as this across a number of areas of mathematics, students can begin to see the links between topics and don't have to remember which visualisation goes with which topic.

Once understanding of calculations with numerical fractions is secure, students can access working with algebraic fractions, which is essential to higher-level mathematics.

Continued fractions

In the spirit of enhancing our subject knowledge, let's take a look at something outside the standard school curriculum, but which has interesting links to topics throughout this book. This is the relatively uncommon way of representing a number via a **continued fraction**, which is a fraction of the form

$$a + \cfrac{1}{b + \cfrac{1}{c + \cfrac{1}{d}}}$$

where the numbers a, b, c, etc. are called the **partial denominators** and fractions are nested within other fractions.

We can demonstrate the process of writing a continued fraction with the number $\frac{27}{5}$ or 5.4. This is $5 + \frac{2}{5}$. Now we use the fact that the **reciprocal,** or multiplicative inverse, of $\frac{2}{5}$ is $\frac{5}{2}$, since $\frac{2}{5} \times \frac{5}{2} = 1$. Since each numerator in our continued fraction is 1 (we call these *unit fractions*), we need to write $\frac{2}{5}$ as $\frac{1}{\frac{5}{2}}$, so our $5 + \frac{2}{5}$ becomes $5 + \frac{1}{\frac{5}{2}}$ or $5 + \frac{1}{2 + \frac{1}{2}}$. Since the last fraction is a unit fraction, we stop.

Now let's consider the same process with a fraction that produces a recurring decimal, say, $\frac{25}{7}$.

$$\frac{25}{7} = 3 + \frac{4}{7} = 3 + \frac{1}{\frac{7}{4}} = 3 + \frac{1}{1 + \frac{3}{4}} = 3 + \frac{1}{1 + \frac{1}{\frac{4}{3}}} = 3 + \frac{1}{1 + \frac{1}{1 + \frac{1}{3}}}$$

In Section 2.3 we will pick up the idea of continued fractions in relation to quadratics and irrational numbers.

Index notation and integer indices

Understanding how to evaluate complex expressions is an essential part of a well-developed number sense. Indices in their many forms provide us with an extremely useful way of signifying a number of calculations. **Index** form is indispensable when we begin calculus, so mastering it at an earlier stage is very important.

First, let us introduce some vocabulary. Raising a number to a power is called **exponentiation** and we have the following terms.

$$\underset{\text{base}}{\longrightarrow} 2^5 \underset{}{\longleftarrow} \overset{\text{exponent}}{}$$

Knowing that a positive integer index represents a repeated multiplication, let us pay particular attention to a zero and a negative integer index. Consider the two columns in the table.

Powers of 2	Powers of 5
$2^3 = 8$	$5^3 = 125$
$2^2 = 4$	$5^2 = 25$
$2^1 = 2$	$5^1 = 5$
$2^0 = 1$	$5^0 = 1$
$2^{-1} = \frac{1}{2}$	$5^{-1} = \frac{1}{5}$
$2^{-2} = \frac{1}{4}$	$5^{-2} = \frac{1}{25}$
$2^{-3} = \frac{1}{8}$	$5^{-3} = \frac{1}{125}$

The table illustrates nicely how zero and negative indices work. In the left-hand column, as the index is reduced by 1 the answer is divided by 2. In the right-hand column the answer is divided by 5. Clearly the pattern would hold for any base, and so we have that any number raised to the power of 0 must equal 1, $x^0 \equiv 1$, and that any negative index has the effect of reciprocating the base before applying the power, $x^{-a} \equiv \left(\dfrac{1}{x}\right)^a \equiv \dfrac{1}{x^a}$.[1] Students often write things like $2^0 = 0$ or $2^{-3} = -8$. Demonstrating why this is not the case is an important part of minimising these misconceptions.

This table makes the meaning of exponentiation much clearer. Have you ever described 5^3 along the lines of '5 multiplied by itself three times'? When you stop to consider that sentence, it's not actually true. 5 multiplied by itself three times would be $5 \times 5 \times 5 \times 5$. More accurate would be 'the product of three 5s'. Another approach, which explains both positive and negative indices, would be that for 5^3 you start with 1 and multiply it by 5 three times, and for 5^{-3} you start with 1 and divide it by 5 three times.

At this point it is worth noting the idea of reciprocation in a little more detail. In Section 1.2 we addressed the idea of a multiplicative inverse, the number you multiply by to get an answer of 1. This number is called the reciprocal. For instance, the reciprocal of 2 is $\dfrac{1}{2}$, the reciprocal of 7 is $\dfrac{1}{7}$, and the reciprocal of $\dfrac{2}{3}$ is $\dfrac{1}{\frac{2}{3}}$, or $\dfrac{3}{2}$. We now have an alternative notation for the reciprocal, or multiplicative inverse, in that the reciprocal of x is x^{-1}.

Fractional indices

Before we consider other types of index we need to recall two essential laws.

Law 1: When two numbers, written in index form, have the same base and are multiplied together, add the indices.

$$x^a \times x^b \equiv x^{a+b}$$

For example, $3^4 \times 3^2 = (3 \times 3 \times 3 \times 3) \times (3 \times 3) = 3^6$.

Law 2: When two numbers, written in index form, have the same base and are divided, subtract the indices.

$$\frac{x^a}{x^b} \equiv x^{a-b}$$

For example, $\dfrac{6^7}{6^4} = \dfrac{6 \times 6 \times 6 \times 6 \times 6 \times 6 \times 6}{6 \times 6 \times 6 \times 6} = 6 \times 6 \times 6 = 6^3$.

---

[1] You will have noticed the use of the identity symbol, $\equiv$, here instead of the equals sign, $=$. This will be discussed further in Section 2.1.

Algebraic proof of the law of adding indices	Algebraic proof of the law of subtracting indices
$x^a \times x^b \equiv \left(\underbrace{x \times \ldots \times x}_{a\ \text{times}} \right) \times \left(\underbrace{x \times \ldots \times x}_{b\ \text{times}} \right)$ $\equiv \underbrace{x \times \ldots \times x}_{a+b\ \text{times}}$ $\equiv x^{a+b}$	$\dfrac{x^a}{x^b} \equiv \dfrac{\left(\overbrace{x \times \ldots \times x}^{a\ \text{times}} \right)}{\left(\underbrace{x \times \ldots \times x}_{b\ \text{times}} \right)}$ $\equiv \dfrac{\left(\overbrace{x \times \ldots \times x}^{b\ \text{times}} \right)}{\left(\underbrace{x \times \ldots \times x}_{b\ \text{times}} \right)} \times \dfrac{\left(\overbrace{x \times \ldots \times x}^{a-b\ \text{times}} \right)}{1}$ $\equiv \left(\underbrace{x \times \ldots \times x}_{a-b\ \text{times}} \right)$ $\equiv x^{a-b}$

Now, applying the first law, what number would replace p in the following identity?

$$x^p \times x^p \equiv x$$

Since x can be written x^1, it is evident that $p = \dfrac{1}{2}$, as $x^{\frac{1}{2}} \times x^{\frac{1}{2}} \equiv x^{\frac{1}{2} + \frac{1}{2}} \equiv x^1$. This identity is another way of writing:

$$\sqrt{x} \times \sqrt{x} \equiv x$$

and we see that $x^{\frac{1}{2}} \equiv \sqrt{x}$.

The final types of index to consider are those with non-unit fractions. To do so we need to observe that:

$$\left(x^a \right)^b \equiv x^{ab}$$

For example, $\left(2^3 \right)^4 = 2^3 \times 2^3 \times 2^3 \times 2^3 = 2^{12}$.

Algebraic proof of the law of multiplying indices
$\left(x^a \right)^b \equiv \underbrace{x^a \times \ldots \times x^a}_{b\ \text{times}}$ $\equiv x^{\overbrace{a + \ldots + a}^{b\ \text{times}}}$ $\equiv x^{ab}$

Since any fraction can be written as the product of its numerator and the corresponding unit fraction, we can clearly identify the function of the numerator and denominator in an index.

$$8^{\frac{2}{3}} = 8^{\frac{1}{3} \times 2} = \left(8^{\frac{1}{3}} \right)^2 = (\sqrt[3]{8})^2 = 2^2 = 4$$

More generally, $x^{\frac{p}{q}} \equiv x^{\frac{1}{q} \times p} \equiv \left(\frac{1}{x^{\frac{1}{q}}}\right)^p \equiv (\sqrt[q]{x})^p$.

One useful application of the law of multiplying indices, $(x^a)^b \equiv x^{ab}$, is the ability to change the base of a number. For instance, $9^5 = (3^2)^5 = 3^{10}$. We can evaluate quite awkward-looking numbers with this technique. Take $\dfrac{2^{20}}{4^9 + 8^6}$, for instance. When we notice that 4 and 8 are both powers of 2 we can simplify the calculation like this:

$$\frac{2^{20}}{4^9 + 8^6} = \frac{2^{20}}{(2^2)^9 + (2^3)^6} = \frac{2^{20}}{2^{18} + 2^{18}} = \frac{2^{20}}{2 \times 2^{18}} = \frac{2^{20}}{2^{19}} = 2$$

A question such as this one tests lots of skills in one go. Stop and take another look through all the steps, making a list of all the techniques or knowledge required to get to the right answer. Looking at questions, especially more complex problems, in this way is invaluable when you are in your early stages of teaching, as it helps you to consider the following:

• What am I really asking my students to do?

• Where could they trip up?

• Have I prepared them adequately to answer a question like this?

 1.3b Preparing to teach – do the mathematics!

Try these questions yourself before proceeding

1 Prove algebraically that $(ab)^n \equiv a^n b^n$. What properties of multiplication did you use in your proof?

2 Why is it true that $\left(\dfrac{a}{b}\right)^n \equiv \dfrac{a^n}{b^n}$? Does this work for roots as well? Is it the case that $\sqrt{\dfrac{a}{b}} \equiv \dfrac{\sqrt{a}}{\sqrt{b}}$? Explain your reasoning.

 Further exploration

Logarithms are the inverse of exponentiation (exponents were originally called *antilogarithms*) and open up a world of number and algebra, including a surprising link to the distribution of the prime numbers.

Surds

Surds, or *radicals*, as known in some countries including the US, are irrational numbers that are written in root form. The term can be applied to irrational numbers written as any root, but square roots are the ones dealt with in detail at school. For instance, $\sqrt{16}$ is not a surd, as it is an integer, but $\sqrt{17}$ is.

$$\overset{\text{degree}}{\longrightarrow} \sqrt[3]{5} \longleftarrow \text{radicand}$$

The radical sign was first printed in 1525 in the first ever German algebra textbook, *Die Coss*, by Cristoff Rudolff (incidentally the first printed text to use the signs $+$ and $-$). The actual title of the book is the rather more fabulous *Behend und Hübsch Rechnung durch die kunstreichen regeln Algebre so gemeinicklich die Coss genent werden*, which translates from Old German as *A clever way of calculating sums by the artful rules of algebra commonly called 'the thing'*, the word 'coss' coming from the Italian 'cosa' meaning 'thing'. Nowadays we have such terms as **variable** and **unknown**, which are, essentially, elaborate synonyms of 'thing'.

Surds enable us to write irrational numbers in an exact way, instead of recording the first few digits of an infinite decimal. Being able to work with exact numbers avoids error, and therefore being able to manipulate and work effectively with numbers presented in this form is as important as being fluent with **rational numbers**.

Any surd is easiest to calculate with if it is in its simplest form. We can simplify surds by identifying the largest square factor of the **radicand**, which enables us to compare very different-looking numbers. For instance, should you need to find the sum of $\sqrt{128}$ and $\sqrt{8}$ this would be difficult to envisage were you not aware that $\sqrt{128} = \sqrt{64}\sqrt{2} = 8\sqrt{2}$ and that $\sqrt{8} = \sqrt{4}\sqrt{2} = 2\sqrt{2}$, and therefore that the sum is simply $10\sqrt{2}$.

A number such as $\frac{1}{2}\sqrt{3}$ or $\frac{2}{9}\sqrt{7}$ is also in this useful form – a multiple of a surd – whereas one such as $\frac{5}{\sqrt{6}}$ is not. This number can be transformed to a useful form by a process called **rationalising the denominator** (that is, making the denominator a rational number). The fraction $\frac{1}{\sqrt{2}}$ can be rationalised by multiplying by $\frac{\sqrt{2}}{\sqrt{2}}$ (which is, of course, 1, so the fraction does not change), giving $\frac{\sqrt{2}}{2}$ or $\frac{1}{2}\sqrt{2}$. When the denominator of a fraction is slightly more complex, and consists of two terms, such as $\frac{5}{\sqrt{5}+1}$, we utilise the **difference of two squares,** $(x-y)(x+y) \equiv x^2 - y^2$, to rationalise (more about the difference of two squares in Section 2.1).

$$\frac{5}{\sqrt{5}+1} \times \frac{\sqrt{5}-1}{\sqrt{5}-1} = \frac{5(\sqrt{5}-1)}{5-1} = \frac{5(\sqrt{5}-1)}{4} = \frac{5}{4}(\sqrt{5}-1)$$

In this process we are multiplying the numerator and denominator by the **conjugate** of the denominator; that is, the conjugate of $x+y$ is $x-y$.

 1.3c Preparing to teach – do the mathematics!

Try these questions yourself before proceeding

1 With reference to problem 1.3b, how can we prove that $\sqrt{ab} \equiv \sqrt{a}\sqrt{b}$?

2 Rationalise $\dfrac{12}{6+\sqrt{3}-\sqrt{5}}$.

What about the negative square root?

If you take the square root of any positive number, you get two answers: a positive square root and a negative square root. For example, both 3 and −3 are square roots of 9. This means that if you square either a negative or a positive number, you get a positive answer. It follows that you cannot square root a negative number. (Well, you can, but we'll come to this shortly.) Radical notation, by definition, implies a positive root, so if we write $\sqrt{9}$ we mean 3. To indicate both roots, we write $\pm\sqrt{9}$. Similarly, fractional index notation implies only a positive root, so $25^{\frac{1}{2}} = 5$.

More interestingly, the rule that enables you to combine surds by multiplying, such as $\sqrt{2} \times \sqrt{5} = \sqrt{10}$, cannot apply to negative numbers. Take this pair of examples, firstly with a positive number:

$$6 = \sqrt{6} \times \sqrt{6} = \sqrt{6 \times 6} = \sqrt{36} = 6$$

and secondly with a negative number:

$$-6 = \sqrt{-6} \times \sqrt{-6} = \sqrt{-6 \times -6} = \sqrt{36} = 6$$

This illustrates quite nicely why, in order to avoid ambiguity (and big problems!), radical notation has to be limited to mean the positive root only. It is also a lovely demonstration of how a seemingly logical mathematical process breaks if we misunderstand things, much like the proof that $2 = 1$ in Section 4.3.

The number line

We have referred to many types of number so far, and this is the point at which we consider how these types fit together. When a child learns about number, they learn how to count things they see: one finger, two fingers, and so on. These positive whole numbers are the natural place to begin thinking about number, and we call them the natural numbers. In mathematics, we denote the *set* of the natural numbers with the symbol $\mathbb{N}$ and write $\mathbb{N} = \{1, 2, 3, 4, ...\}$. There is some debate in the mathematics community as to whether or not 0 is a natural number; various sources include and exclude it from the set. We'll exclude it here and consider the natural numbers the 'counting numbers'. If a number is in this set we write $n \in \mathbb{N}$, read 'n is an element of the natural numbers' or simply 'n is in the natural numbers'.

Now, of course, this set of numbers is insufficient once we get past basic counting. Let us add in 0 and the negative whole numbers, which expands our set and creates the set of integers, $\mathbb{Z}$, where $\mathbb{Z} = \{..., -3, -2, -1, 0, 1, 2, 3, ...\}$. The symbol $\mathbb{Z}$ comes from the German word *zahlen*, meaning 'numbers'.

Of course, this still doesn't suit all our number needs. We need to consider parts of a whole so we will add in fractions, or any number that can be written as a fraction (e.g. $\frac{1}{2}$, 0.78, 0.3$\dot{1}$). These numbers, as decimals, are either terminating or recurring and, together with the integers, make the set of rational numbers, $\mathbb{Q}$. The symbol $\mathbb{Q}$ comes from the word **quotient**, the answer to a division. Note that the rational numbers must include the integers, as these can also be written as fractions: $12 = \frac{12}{1}$ or $-2 = -\frac{6}{3}$.

Imagine a number line with every number now mentioned marked off. The line is starting to fill up, but we are missing one important set of numbers: the irrational numbers such as π or $\sqrt{2}$; that is, those numbers that have an infinite decimal expansion containing no repeating pattern and which therefore cannot be written as fractions. If we include these numbers in the number line we have a complete line and we call this set the **real numbers**, $\mathbb{R}$.

Irrational numbers have proven very problematic in history. The Pythagoreans were an ancient mystical sect, a group of men who spent their days measuring and wondering at the beauty of nature and the expanse of the cosmos, resolute in their belief that the universe could be explained and deciphered using mathematics. They were masters of geometry and sought to understand the workings of the world by analysing numbers and shapes and the intersection of the two. One of the Pythagoreans' core beliefs was that any number could be written as the ratio of two others in the way that 6 is $\frac{12}{2}$, or 2.$\dot{3}$ is $\frac{7}{3}$. It felt complete, it felt perfect. But for the

Pythagoreans, perfection was about to be shattered. Perhaps the greatest discovery of the Pythagoreans was what we now call Pythagoras' theorem, where the square of the hypotenuse of a right-angled triangle is equal to the sum of the squares of the other two sides. In a cruel twist of fate it was this very discovery that eroded the foundations of the Pythagoreans' tower of mathematical knowledge.

Imagine you have a right-angled isosceles triangle where the two **perpendicular** sides have length 1. Then, by the theorem, the hypotenuse is equal to $\sqrt{2}$. So, the square root of 2 can be drawn and therefore must be a line of finite length.

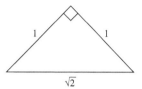

Figure 1.16

The problem arises, so legend goes, when one of the sect's members, a man called Hippasus, was able to prove that $\sqrt{2}$ *cannot* be written as the ratio of two other numbers (that is, as a fraction). So not only is it not of finite length, but it has no repeating patterns. It is what we call an irrational number. What a blow! The world as they believed it to be, in all its predictable glory, was shattered. So Hippasus, who according to some reports was on a ship at the time, was unceremoniously thrown overboard. Imagine that: murdered for discovering a new type of number.

The proof that $\sqrt{2}$ is irrational is an example of a **proof by contradiction** that brings together many of the elements we've looked at so far in Chapter 1. In a proof by contradiction we assume a statement true, follow through from this assumption, come to a contradiction, and therefore conclude that our original assumption was false. Let's start by assuming that $\sqrt{2}$ is a rational number, and therefore can be written as a fraction in its simplest terms.

$$\text{Let } \sqrt{2} = \frac{p}{q}.$$

Since this fraction is simplified, we know that p and q are coprime. Now we will square both sides of this equation.

$$2 = \frac{p^2}{q^2}$$
$$\Rightarrow 2q^2 = p^2$$

This statement tells us that p^2 is even, as it is a multiple of 2. Now, if a square number is even, then its square root is even. This is a consequence of the fundamental theorem of arithmetic – if 2 is a factor of p^2, then it must also be a factor of p. This means p is even, so we can write p as a multiple of 2. Let's say $p = 2m$, and substitute this into our last line.

$$2q^2 = (2m)^2 = 4m^2$$
$$\Rightarrow q^2 = 2m^2$$

Now we conclude in the same way that q^2 must be even, so q must be even. But here's the contradiction: if both p and q are even, then our original fraction, $\dfrac{p}{q}$, could have been simplified, so it wasn't in its simplest terms. That means our assumption, that $\sqrt{2}$ could be written as a simplified fraction, was wrong and $\sqrt{2}$ cannot be a rational number.

 1.3d Preparing to teach – do the mathematics!

Try this question yourself before proceeding
Following the example of $\sqrt{2}$, prove that $\sqrt{3}$ is an irrational number.

Let's get back to our sets of numbers. Note that every set contains the one before it. For instance, 5 is a natural number, an integer, a rational number and a real number. We signify this using set notation and the symbol $\subset$ is read 'is a subset of'.

$$\mathbb{N} \subset \mathbb{Z} \subset \mathbb{Q} \subset \mathbb{R}$$

For the vast majority of mathematical history most people were happy that this represented a complete picture of the numbers. In the sixteenth century, however, men such as Gerolamo Cardano and Rafael Bombelli told us that it was indeed possible to square root a negative number if we only extended our concept of number. René Descartes (he of the Cartesian grid, see Section 2.3) was dismissive of the idea, calling these numbers 'imaginary'. The name stuck and the idea took hold. Leonhard Euler used the notation i for $\sqrt{-1}$ in the eighteenth century and the study of **imaginary numbers** took off. As much as the ancients couldn't comprehend the ideas of negative numbers, zero or irrational numbers, even though they clearly exist, so many people today cannot comprehend the idea of imaginary numbers, even though they exist and have many applications in fields throughout mathematics, engineering and computer science, to name a few. The addition of the imaginary numbers to the set of real numbers produces our final set of numbers, the **complex numbers**, $\mathbb{C}$, and here we must stop.

Further exploration

The complex numbers are studied in some depth in advanced mathematics. They are an intrinsic part of trigonometry and its myriad applications, being used to represent alternating currents in electrical engineering, for instance.

Famous irrational numbers

Some numbers are so very interesting that they deserve their own section in a book like this. Arguably the most interesting number is 0 – and people have written entire books on that one – but we will stick to irrational numbers here, and two of them in particular: π and e.

π is famously known as the **constant** that links the circumference of a circle to its diameter in the relationship $C = \pi d$, or the area to the radius in $A = \pi r^2$. It has been approximated throughout the centuries with increasing accuracy. Our earliest known recordings of it date from the ancient Babylonians and Egyptians around 1600 BCE, who had it pinned between 3.1 and 3.2 and, as of 2016, modern computers had calculated the number to over 22 trillion digits, almost all of which are redundant in any practical calculation – even NASA uses no more than 16 digits for interplanetary calculations.

But there is so much more to π than being simply a constant of proportionality, and this is because circles are everywhere, even when you don't realise it. Take the probability experiment commonly known as Buffon's needle, named after the eighteenth century French aristocrat and mathematician Georges-Louis Leclerc, Comte de Buffon. The experiment asks you to drop a stick or needle-like object onto floorboards and asks what the probability is of the needle landing on a crack between two boards. Buffon proved that, in the case where the needles are shorter than the width of the floorboards, the probability of landing across a gap is $\dfrac{2l}{\pi x}$, where l is the length of the needle and x is the width of the floorboards. It may seem strange at first that π should appear in this **formula**, but consider for a moment what shape is made when you rotate a stick.

Circles and curvature are everywhere, and where there are circles there is π. You will find that practically any area of life that involves mathematical calculations – science, engineering, economics, geography – has formulae that use π. Wave or pendulum models in fluid dynamics, electronics, architecture or sound engineering use it; population growth and decay models use it; aircraft designers and even medical researchers use it (think how many body parts feature curvature close to that of circles or spheres, such as the cross-section of a bone, or the eye).

The irrational number e is equally as fascinating as π and turns up in almost as many places, although it doesn't benefit from the stellar fame of its cousin, since it is not introduced until more advanced courses than the majority of students experiences. $e \approx 2.718$ (to 3 decimal places) and is known as the *exponential constant*. Discovered by Leonhard Euler (the same guy who introduced i for $\sqrt{-1}$), it plays an important role in any calculation involving exponential growth.

To demonstrate, let's consider what happens when you deposit money in a bank account that earns interest. The bank compounds interest, so as your money increases, so does the interest paid by the bank on this money. What happens if your bank calculates the interest monthly? Do you get more money if your bank calculates it weekly or daily? If it calculates and adds the interest more frequently, does the amount of interest paid grow infinitely large? To answer this question we'll do some calculations and keep the numbers simple. Recall that to increase an investment by 5% we multiply by 1.05, or to increase by 60% we multiply by 1.6, so to increase by 100% we multiply by 2.

Imagine you invest £1 and the bank pays 100% interest per year. After 1 year you will have £1 $\times 2 = £2$. Now, if the bank pays this 100% in two 50% instalments, then after 1 year you will have $£1 \times (1 + \frac{1}{2})^2 = £1 \times 1.5^2 = £2.25$. If the bank pays the interest in three 33.$\dot{3}$% instalments, then after 1 year you will have $£1 \times (1 + \frac{1}{3})^3 = £1 \times 1.\dot{3}^3 = £2.37$. Let's continue the pattern.

Number of instalments per year	Calculation	Balance after 1 year
1 (yearly)	$£1 \times (1 + 1)^1$	£2
2 (biannually)	$£1 \times \left(1 + \frac{1}{2}\right)^2$	£2.25
3 (triannually)	$£1 \times \left(1 + \frac{1}{3}\right)^3$	£2.3704
4 (quarterly)	$£1 \times \left(1 + \frac{1}{4}\right)^4$	£2.4414
12 (monthly)	$£1 \times \left(1 + \frac{1}{12}\right)^{12}$	£2.6130
52 (weekly)	$£1 \times \left(1 + \frac{1}{52}\right)^{52}$	£2.6926

Number of instalments per year	Calculation	Balance after 1 year
365 (daily)	$£1 \times \left(1 + \dfrac{1}{365}\right)^{365}$	£2.7146
8760 (hourly)	$£1 \times \left(1 + \dfrac{1}{8760}\right)^{8760}$	£2.7181
525 600 (each minute)	$£1 \times \left(1 + \dfrac{1}{525600}\right)^{525600}$	£2.7183

You certainly get more money if the interest is paid more frequently, but this number doesn't get infinitely big. In fact, the sequence of values is converging to a limit, and that limit is e. e occurs in formulae in thermodynamics, electrodynamics, models of growth and decay and much more, and in Section 4.2 we will see another of its amazing properties.

Finally, no chapter on numbers that mentions e, π and i would be complete without a nod to Euler's identity which is possibly the greatest equation in the history of mathematics and a thing of beauty. To this point we have considered the importance of the additive identity, 0, the multiplicative identity, 1, the square root of −1, i, and the two most prolific irrational numbers, e and π. Just imagine if all these numbers were somehow linked; what a wonderfully complete equation that would be (you can see where this is going!). Well, they are linked, and here it is:

$$e^{i\pi} + 1 = 0$$

We can take the product of an irrational number with an imaginary number, raise another irrational number to the power of this product and get the value of −1. Mind-blowingly simple in its complexity, this is the queen of equations.

 Further exploration

Angles and turning are intrinsically part of the study of circles and curvature. Once students begin to study advanced mathematics they will measure angles not in degrees, but in radians, which is a unit of measure that takes a full turn as 2π, so any other turn is a fraction of this. A quarter turn of 90°, for instance, is $\dfrac{2\pi}{4} = \dfrac{\pi}{2}$ in radians. Why was a radian chosen to be the size it is, and why does this result in a full turn being 2π? Why are radians essential in calculus?

Quiz 1

1. Explain the difference between a digit, a numeral and a number.

2. Identify which digits in the following numbers are significant and not significant and, in addition, identify which zeros are placeholders and which are not.

   a. 7850 (correct to 3 s.f.)

   b. 0.605 (correct to 3 s.f.)

   c. 0.025 030 (correct to 5 s.f.)

   d. 40 900 (correct to 4 s.f.)

3. How many zeros are there at the end of the number $2^3 \times 3^2 \times 4^5 \times 5^8 \times 6$?

4. In Problem 1.2c we used divisibility rules to work out which single-digit numbers 378 000 is divisible by. How can we answer this question using the prime factor decomposition of 378 000?

5. What is the smallest integer you can multiply by 1032 to give a square product?

6. Replace the symbols in the following number with digits to make it divisible by 15.

$$27*75*$$

   How many ways are there to do this?

7. What is the final digit in the answer to $9^{56} + 9^{55}$?

8. Which set(s) of numbers do the following belong to?

   a. -35

   b. 1.7

   c. $\dfrac{4}{5}$

   d. 0

9. Explain the process that takes 0.8^{-2} to an answer of 1.5625.

10. Write, as a single power of 6, $6^7 + 6^7 + 6^7 + 6^7 + 6^7 + 6^7$.

11. There are three steps involved when evaluating $\left(\dfrac{49}{25}\right)^{-\frac{5}{2}}$. Should they be performed in a particular order?

12. If $9^x = 64$, what does 27^x equal? What about 27^{2x}? Write 27^{2x} in the form 2^n, where n is an integer to be found.

The next three questions move well beyond the school curriculum but only require school-level mathematics to complete.

13. Find the decimal representation of $1 + \dfrac{1}{2 + \frac{1}{3 + \frac{1}{4}}}$.

14. In other bases, parts of a whole are still written after a decimal point. In denary the columns after the decimal point represent the values tenths, hundredths, thousandths and so on, which can be written $\dfrac{1}{10^1}$, $\dfrac{1}{10^2}$, $\dfrac{1}{10^3}$,... . In binary, the number 0.625, or $\dfrac{5}{8}$, can be 'built up' using negative powers of 2 ($\dfrac{1}{2}$, $\dfrac{1}{4}$, $\dfrac{1}{8}$, etc.) and we need to work out what sum of these will create our fraction. We start with $1 \times \dfrac{1}{2}$ but if we add $\dfrac{1}{4}$ we have passed $\dfrac{5}{8}$. If we add $\dfrac{1}{8}$ we have now reached $\dfrac{5}{8}$ and can stop. This means we have $\dfrac{5}{8} = 1 \times \dfrac{1}{2} + 0 \times \dfrac{1}{4} + 1 \times \dfrac{1}{8} = 0.101_2$, where the subscript '2' tells us this answer is in base 2.

Now write the following numbers in binary.

a. 0.25

b. 0.0625

c. 0.3125

d. 0.3

15. The numbers given are in base ten. Convert them all to binary and evaluate the calculations using traditional column methods or long/short division.

a. $25 + 13$

b. 24×10

c. $112 - 87$

d. $48 \div 12$

Answers to each Quiz, Try this first *and* Preparing to teach *are at the back of the book.*

Chapter 2

Algebra I: Expressions, equations and graphs

2.1 Expressions and conventions

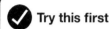

Try this first

1. What is the difference between an **expression**, an **equation** and a **formula**?

2. What does it mean to '**factorise**' an expression? Why is this terminology used? What is the point of factorising?

The Persian mathematician al-Khwarizmi, who lived during the ninth century, provided a systematic way of solving linear and **quadratic** equations, in which the word *al-Jabr* first appears. This word refers to the process of 'balancing' an equation by subtracting the same amount from either side. It is from this word that we get our term *algebra*.

The origins of algebra cannot be traced to one place. It is the culmination of centuries of mathematical thought, encompassing the ideas of the ancient Egyptians and Babylonians, who solved equations using numerical methods such as interpolation; the Greeks, who thought geometrically; the Chinese, who were experts in numerical patterns and infinite series; the Indians, who were rigorous in number systems and linear and quadratic equations; and the Arabs, who went on to solve much more complex equations and introduced much of the notation we use today for numbers, including fractions.

Algebra as we know it began its formalisation at the end of the sixteenth century by mathematicians from various parts of Europe, who drew on the work of those who preceded them. It developed from there into the essential force behind mathematics that we know today. The ability to manipulate and work with unknown quantities enables us to understand and to model the world, ushering in the most modern applications of mathematics, such as statistics, computing and engineering.

In school we introduce algebra from the very foundations, helping students to understand how to manipulate symbols and solve some of the simplest types of equation. Algebra allows us to work with **unknowns**, which in turn enables us to create mathematical models in hundreds of fields, from biology to meteorology, to finance, to computing, to engineering, to architecture, to chemistry, to medicine and beyond. Algebra underpins our modern world and has allowed us to create the complex society that we inhabit.

Conventions and vocabulary

The first thing we meet when starting to learn algebra is the expression. An expression is a combination of **variables** (letters that can represent any value)**, constants** (fixed numbers) and operators. So when we learn that $a + a$ can be simplified to $2a$ we are starting to work with expressions. When constants and variables are multiplied or divided we create a **term**, and when terms are added or subtracted we create an expression. The following are all examples of expressions.

$2x$	[one term]
$3y^{\frac{1}{2}} - 5$	[two terms]
$pq^3 \times \dfrac{5}{q^{-4}}$	[one term]
$2x^2 - 7x + 1$	[three terms]
$(2x - 6)(3x + 2)^2$	[one term, composed of two brackets, each containing two terms]
$\int \sin t \cos^3 t\, dt$	[one term]

Some of these expressions are examples of **polynomials**, some are not. A polynomial is an algebraic expression containing constants and variables; and the operations of addition, subtraction and multiplication (but not division of variables); and non-negative **integer** powers. A single-term polynomial is called a monomial, two terms a **binomial**, three a trinomial (and *very* rarely you might come across quadrinomial for four terms). The **degree** or **order** of a polynomial is the highest power of any term in the polynomial. If the polynomial has terms where different letters are multiplied together, we must **sum** the **indices** to obtain the degree of the term. Thus $x^2 + 2x - 1$ is a polynomial of degree 2 and $2a^2y^3 - 6a^3$ is a polynomial of degree 5, since the first term has degree 5 and the second term has degree 3.

 2.1a Preparing to teach – do the mathematics!

Try this question yourself before proceeding

Sort the six expressions listed above into two columns: *polynomial,* and *not polynomial*. For the polynomials, identify what type of -nomial they are (mo-, bi-, tri-) and state the degree of the polynomial.

In the mathematics classroom we practise manipulating expressions with processes such as collecting **like terms**, simplifying and rewriting indices, **rationalising denominators**, simplifying **surds**, factorising and expanding, and simplifying algebraic fractions. In order to manipulate expressions effectively our students need to be at home with certain (arbitrary) conventions and some of these take longer than you might think to become habitual. Some of the conventions we teachers can take for granted, but which need to be explained clearly, are not writing a multiplication symbol $(2 \times x \equiv 2x)$, using a fraction bar instead of the division symbol $(x \div 5 \equiv \frac{x}{5})$ and not writing a **coefficient** of 1 $(1x \equiv x)$.

You will have noticed the use of the **identity** symbol, $\equiv$, above. This much-underused symbol is often replaced with the much-overused equals sign, $=$, which becomes a gap filler in lines of work. Don't be surprised if you see atrocities like this:

Solve the equation $2x + 3 = 12$.

$$2x + 3 = 12 - 3 = 9 \div 2 = 4.5$$

The difference between usage of each symbol is subtle but important. If two expressions are always equal to each other, no matter the value of the variables, then the statement is an identity. Thus, since $x + x + x$ is always identical to $3x$, regardless of the value of x, we should use the identity symbol and write $x + x + x \equiv 3x$. On the other hand, since $5x - 3$ is only equal to 10 in the single case where $x = \frac{13}{5}$, we use an equals sign: $5x - 3 = 10$.

In reality, the equals sign is often used for both identities and **equations**, whereas the identity symbol can *never* be used for equations. Making more use of the identity symbol can help you to formalise the difference between an identity (which is always true) and an equation (which is sometimes true).

 Discuss

Why might it be important to be strict about the use of the identity symbol over the equals sign? What benefits or disadvantages are there to using it wherever it is appropriate?

 2.1b Preparing to teach – do the mathematics!

Try this question yourself before proceeding

Sort the following thirteen statements into three columns: *always true*, *sometimes true* and *never true*. Replace the equals sign with $\equiv$ or $\neq$ where appropriate.

$n^2 = 2n$ $\qquad\qquad$ $x^2 > 10$ $\qquad\qquad$ $n^2 \geq n$

$16m^2 = (4m)^2$ $\qquad\qquad$ $n - 2 = \dfrac{1}{10}$ $\qquad\qquad$ $X + 2 = Y + 2$

$3(x + 1) = 3x + 1$ $\qquad\qquad$ $3(x + 1) = 3x + 3$ $\qquad\qquad$ $x^2 + 25 = 0$

$a - 3 = a - 7$ $\qquad\qquad$ $x^{\frac{1}{2}} = \sqrt{x}$ $\qquad\qquad$ $a - b = b - a$

$pqr = rqp$

This is an example of an activity that can be done with many topics. A quick Internet search for 'always, sometimes, never' will lead you to plenty of examples you can use in the classroom.

Two words that are often used interchangeably are the words **variable** and **unknown**. Both are represented, not exclusively, by letters such as x, y and z (see Section 2.3 for why), but they are subtly different. Understanding the difference enables us to model the precision we aim to see from our students. To illustrate this, consider the difference between the following equations.

$$3x + 1 = -5$$
$$2x + 3y = 9$$

In the first equation, many people would say that the numbers 3, 1 and −5 are constants and x is a variable. Similarly, in the second equation, many would say that 2, 3 and 9 are constants and x and y are variables. Consider both equations again, though. The first equation has one solution, $x = -2$, which means x can be more accurately thought of as an *unknown constant*, or simply an *unknown*, in this case. In contrast, the second equation has infinitely many solution pairs. Either x or y could take any value, producing a corresponding value for the other, so in this case x and y are *variables*: their value can vary.

In practice, unknowns are a type of variable, in the instance where the variable could be calculated. For this reason many people use the two terms interchangeably in equations, although in an expression such as $5x - 4$, you would be stretching it to call x an unknown, as it really can vary infinitely with no constraints[1].

---

[1] If we're being *really* pedantic it could also be argued that, in an equation of the form $y = 2x + 3$, once a value is picked for the variable x, then y becomes an unknown, since its value could be computed. In this case, some people prefer the terms *independent variable* (for x) and *dependent variable* (for y), as its value depends on that chosen for x, although this wording is rarely heard outside a statistics class. And sometimes pedantry is unnecessary.

Adding, subtracting, multiplying and dividing terms

In its rawest sense, algebra is a generalisation of number, thus expressions generalise the interactions of numbers. Consider the following.

$$1+1+1 = 3 \times 1$$
$$2+2+2 = 3 \times 2$$
$$5+5+5 = 3 \times 5$$
$$x+x+x \equiv 3 \times x \equiv 3x$$

The final algebraic identity sums up, in one line, what we could write out forever using numbers: that 'number + number + number' is always equal to three times that number. By writing $3x$ in place of $x+x+x$ we are simplifying the expression. Consider:

$$2+2+5-2+5+5 = (1 \times 2) + (3 \times 5)$$
$$7+7+8-7+8+8 = (1 \times 7) + (3 \times 8)$$
$$-1+-1+4--1+4+4 = (1 \times -1) + (3 \times 4)$$
$$a+a+b-a+b+b \equiv (1 \times a) + (3 \times b) \equiv a + 3b$$

In each instance we have two numbers (or variables) and can collect together those that are the same. These are called like terms. We cannot collect unlike terms, so the last example cannot be $4ab$, just like the first example cannot be $4 \times 2 \times 5$. This just doesn't make any sense (although you will see it written enough times during your career).

When adding and subtracting we are thinking along the lines of 'how many of [term] do we have?'. When multiplying and dividing we must remember the rules of indices (which we covered in Section 1.3). The beauty of generalising with algebra is that explanations for things like the rules of indices become very clear. For instance, we can combine subtraction of indices and the fact that anything divided by itself is 1 to show that $x^0 \equiv 1$:

$$\frac{x^a}{x^a} \equiv 1 \text{ but } \frac{x^a}{x^a} \equiv x^{a-a} \equiv x^0, \text{ so } x^0 \equiv 1$$

Consider also the **distributive** law, where we know that 35×8 can be calculated by $30 \times 8 + 5 \times 8$. Of course, 35×8 can be written as $(30+5) \times 8$, so we have that:

$$35 \times 8 = (30+5) \times 8 = 30 \times 8 + 5 \times 8$$

which is simply a numerical version of what we commonly call *expanding* brackets:

$$a(x+y) \equiv ax + ay$$

Expanding brackets

Sometimes, expressions are easier to work with in expanded form (such as when we are differentiating and integrating in advanced mathematics), and sometimes we need them in **factorised** form (such as when we are simplifying algebraic fractions). It all depends on what we are trying to achieve, so fluency with the two-way process of expanding and factorising is essential.

Expanding brackets is a process of generalising multiplication, as we saw previously. Consider $(x+a)(y+b)$, where we know we must multiply everything in the first bracket by everything in the second bracket to get $xy+bx+ay+ab$. A numerical analogy to this would be something like 25×87. Whether you multiply these numbers with a column method or a grid, you can see that the process amounts to $(20+5)(80+7)$, with each of the calculations of 20×80, 20×7, 5×80 and 5×7 taking place.

There are a number of ways of demonstrating the process of expanding brackets to students, all of which boil down to different visual representations of the same technique. There are two processes that lend themselves to greater backwards clarity when factorising brackets is introduced – by this I mean that the process is clear in both directions: expanding and factorising. The first of these is to show through an interim step that the second bracket must be multiplied by every term in the first.

$$(x+a)(y+b) \equiv x(y+b) + a(y+b)$$
$$\equiv xy + bx + ay + ab$$

The second is a multiplication grid, where summing all the 'answer' squares produces the correct expression.

x	x	a
y	xy	ay
b	bx	ab

You may see curved lines drawn between terms in the brackets, which ensure that no individual multiplication is missed out, but this alone does not particularly help us when reversing the process by factorising.

Sometimes called the parrot's beak	Sometimes called the smiley face
$(x+a)(y+b) \equiv xy + bx + ay + ab$	$(x+a)(y+b) \equiv xy + ab + ay + bx$

It can be useful to consider multiplication of expressions like this in terms of the area of rectangles. If, for instance, we have a rectangle of length x

and width y, then its area is xy. The multiplication of $(x+a)(y+b)$ has a geometric representation, shown in Figure 2.1, that works a little like a grid multiplication, but which makes clear the need to sum terms in order to find the area of a large rectangle whose sides are of length $x+a$ and $y+b$.

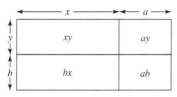

Figure 2.1

This geometric representation continues its usefulness when we complete the square on a quadratic expression, as we will see later.

It is important for students to quickly recognise common forms of expansion. One of these is referred to as the **difference of two squares**, where:

$$(x+y)(x-y) \equiv x^2 + xy - xy - y^2 \equiv x^2 - y^2$$

This crops up again and again in algebraic manipulation of various forms and is an important result for students to be instantly familiar with. It appears in various guises, from the straightforward $x^2 - 16$ to the more advanced $\sin^4\theta - \cos^4\theta$.

Other common expansions are the perfect squares $(x+y)^2 \equiv x^2 + 2xy + y^2$ and $(x-y)^2 \equiv x^2 - 2xy + y^2$. Particular care must be taken over a squared bracket. It is very common for students to write that $(x+3)^2 \equiv x^2 + 9$, for example (and its related error, when dealing with surds, that $\sqrt{9+4} = \sqrt{9} + \sqrt{4}$). You will need to regularly remind students that a squared bracket is in fact the **product** of two brackets.

The process of expanding brackets can be extended to any number of brackets, and any number of terms in a bracket, and we can perform our multiplications in any order due to **commutativity**. If we have multiple brackets we must expand two at a time and then repeat.

 2.1c Preparing to teach – do the mathematics!

Try these questions yourself before proceeding

1 Expand and simplify $(1+x)(1+x+x^2)$.

2 Expand and simplify $(3-x-y)^2$, using $(a-b)^2 \equiv a^2 - 2ab + b^2$.

If we multiply the same bracket repeatedly, such as $(2+3x)^2$ or $(1+\frac{1}{2}x)^8$, then we have a particularly clever way of performing the expansion, which encompasses one of those times when seemingly unrelated mathematical curiosities turn out to be interwoven. We are considering here the **binomial expansion**.

Take a look at this expansion.

$$\begin{aligned}
(1+x)^3 &\equiv (1+x)(1+x)(1+x) \\
&\equiv (1+2x+x^2)(1+x) \\
&\equiv 1+x+2x+2x^2+x^2+x^3 \\
&\equiv 1+3x+3x^2+x^3
\end{aligned}$$

If we write the terms in increasing order of power of x, from x^0 to x^3, then the coefficients of each term go 1, 3, 3, 1.

If we perform a similar expansion, but this time raising our binomial $1+x$ to the power of 4, then the coefficients will go 1, 4, 6, 4, 1:

$$(1+x)^4 \equiv 1+4x+6x^2+4x^3+x^4$$

On the face of it, there is nothing interesting about these numbers, but a little dip into some mathematical history shows them to be quite special. Ancient Indian mathematicians as far back as the second century were aware of them and their interesting properties. If we fast forward to Persia in the eleventh century we meet Omar Khayyam, a mathematician, astronomer and poet who wrote about a triangle of numbers, starting with 1 at the top vertex, where subsequent rows are made by adding the two numbers above, as shown in Figure 2.2.

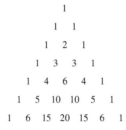

Figure 2.2

In Iran, this is known as Khayyam's triangle. In China, the triangle was popularised in the thirteenth century through a text by the mathematician Yang Hui, and is hence known as Yang Hui's triangle. In the West it is known as Pascal's triangle, after the French mathematician Blaise Pascal, who wrote about it and its many uses in the seventeenth century text *Traité du Triangle Arithmétique*, translated as *Treatise on the Arithmetical Triangle*. Pascal himself was a sickly genius, who died at the age of 39, having made a considerable impact on a number of areas of mathematics, philosophy and theology.

In the triangle, each successive row gives you the coefficients of successive expansions of $(1+x)^n$. If we call the first row the zeroth row, then this has the trivial case of the expansion of $(1+x)^0$, which is, of course, 1. Looking then at the sixth row, we know the expansion of $(1+x)^6$ must be $1 + 6x + 15x^2 + 20x^3 + 15x^4 + 6x^5 + x^6$.

There is a beautiful symmetry in these coefficients and Pascal's triangle hides plenty of other patterns, one of which we will meet in Section 4.1.

 Further exploration

The importance of binomial expansions becomes more apparent as you pursue more advanced mathematics. The expansions and the coefficients in Pascal's triangle can be extended into the realms of probability and combinatorics, where we find the *binomial distribution*. It therefore has several applications stemming from probability theory, not least in medicine and business.

 Discuss

It can be very helpful if all teachers in a department take the same approach to expanding (and factorising) bracketed expressions. What benefit is to be gained from having a standardised approach? Are there times when different approaches can be helpful? Which approaches do you and your colleagues prefer and why?

Factorising expressions

Factorising is the opposite of expanding: putting the brackets back into an expression. It is the algebraic equivalent of writing $12 = 2 \times 6$ – where we can write a number as the product of two others (its **factors**) we can also write an expression as the product of two others (its factors). Just as we can manipulate and simplify numerical expressions when we know the factors of a number, so we can manipulate and simplify algebraic expressions when we factorise them.

A factorised expression is often considered to be in its simplest form, so an expression such as $2x + 6y$ is not as pleasing to the mathematical eye as $2(x+3y)$; and an expression is considered simplest when it is *fully* factorised, so factorising $12x^2 + 4x$ into $4(3x^2 + x)$ is not as complete as factorising into $4x(3x+1)$.

Factorising is essential to later processes in areas such as calculus and trigonometry. Good command of these skills is a solid foundation on which to build more advanced mathematics.

Factorising into a single bracket, by taking out the highest common factor of each term in an expression, is quite straightforward, but more is involved when we factorise polynomials of higher degree, such as quadratics and **cubics**. Let's take a quadratic such as $6x^2 + x - 12$ (which is called a quadratic from the Latin *quadratum,* meaning 'square') and consider that it must factorise into two brackets of the form $(mx+n)(px+q)$. We know that the product of n and q will produce the term of -12, and we know that the product of mx and px will produce the term of $6x^2$, but the middle term of x is harder to work with.

In order to tackle this, we find the product of the coefficients of the first and last terms, in this case -72, and we look for two numbers whose product is this and whose sum is the coefficient of x, in this case 1. These numbers are -8 and 9, since $-8 \times 9 = -72$ and $-8 + 9 = 1$.

$$\text{product is } 6 \times -12, \text{ or } -72$$
$$\text{sum is } 1 \quad 6x^2 + x - 12$$

We now rewrite our quadratic by splitting up the middle term of x into $-8x + 9x$, so we have:

$$6x^2 + x - 12 \equiv 6x^2 - 8x + 9x - 12$$

Now we can factorise successive pairs of terms like this:

$$6x^2 - 8x + 9x - 12 \equiv 2x(3x-4) + 3(3x-4)$$

Looking at this new expression, each of the two terms contains a factor of $3x - 4$, which we factorise out, just as we would a single letter or number. To make the idea of factorising out a multi-term expression clearer, we can use a **vinculum** – a straight line over the expression. This groups the terms together and indicates that the expression is to be treated as one entity.

$$2x(\overline{3x-4}) + 3(\overline{3x-4}) \equiv (\overline{3x-4})(2x+3)$$

This is the backwards application of the method of expanding we considered earlier. The same end can be achieved with a grid expansion; identifying that x should be written as $-8x + 9x$ we populate a grid as in the following.

x	
$6x^2$	$-8x$
$9x$	-12

We then factorise across the first row, removing the common factor of $2x$, before working through what the other empty boxes must contain using the fact that this is a multiplication grid.

x		
$2x$	$6x^2$	$-8x$
	$9x$	-12

x	$3x$	
$2x$	$6x^2$	$-8x$
	$9x$	-12

x	$3x$	
$2x$	$6x^2$	$-8x$
3	$9x$	-12

x	$3x$	-4
$2x$	$6x^2$	$-8x$
3	$9x$	-12

This leaves us with the factorisation of $(3x-4)(2x+3)$.

But when we are factorising the general quadratic, $ax^2 + bx + c$, why do we search for two numbers whose product is ac and whose sum is b? Let's consider the factorised form $(mx+n)(px+q)$ and expand this.

$$(mx+n)(px+q) \equiv mpx^2 + mqx + npx + nq$$

Now, compare this to the general quadratic.

$$mpx^2 + mqx + npx + nq \equiv ax^2 + bx + c$$

By comparing coefficients of x^2, x and x^0 on each side of the identity we can see that:

$$a = mp$$
$$b = mq + np$$
$$c = nq$$

This means we are looking for a pair of numbers whose sum is b, each number being mq and np. Knowing we are looking for such a pair alone is not sufficient – there are infinitely many pairs of numbers whose sum is b. But notice that if we multiply these two numbers together we get $mqnp = mp \times nq = ac$ and we have another condition on the two numbers we are looking for: their product must be ac.

So now we have it: our x term must be split using two numbers whose sum is b and whose product is ac, and the rest is history (or mathematics).

At this point spare a moment to consider the quadratic where $a = 1$, such as $x^2 - 7x - 30$. This is the kind of factorising we tend to teach first, where our students search for two numbers whose product is -30 and whose sum is -7. But, if you hadn't already realised, this is merely a special case of what we have just looked at, where $ac = c$.

The idea of looking for common factors is key when considering more complex expressions. Take, for instance, $xyz - z - 2 + 2yx$. On first glance it may not seem that this expression can be factorised, but if we start to look for terms with common factors something interesting happens. Let's use commutativity and rewrite the expression as $xyz + 2yx - z - 2$. Now look at the common factors in the first and second pairs of terms.

$$xyz + 2yx - z - 2 \equiv xy(z+2) - (z+2)$$
$$\equiv (z+2)(xy-1)$$

Here we employed the handy trick of factorising -1 out of the last two terms, which made it all possible.

 2.1d Preparing to teach – do the mathematics!

Try these questions yourself before proceeding

Factorise:

 $x^4 y^2 - x^4 - x^3 y^2 + x^3$

 $1 + 2a + 2b + a^2 + 2ab + b^2$

Algebraic fractions

Knowing the factors of numbers helps us with many things, not least simplifying fractions. The same ideas can be generalised with algebraic fractions: provided you can divide both numerator and denominator by a common factor, you can simplify the fraction.

Consider $\dfrac{x^4 - 4x^2}{x^3 - 9x^2 - 22x}$, which looks like a pretty complicated fraction. Once we factorise the expressions in the numerator and denominator, however, it simplifies nicely.

$$\frac{x^4 - 4x^2}{x^3 - 9x^2 - 22x} \equiv \frac{x^2(x^2 - 4)}{x(x^2 - 9x - 22)} \equiv \frac{x^2(x-2)(x+2)}{x(x+2)(x-11)} \equiv \frac{x(x-2)}{x-11}$$

Indeed, anything we can do with numerical fractions has an algebraic analogue. We can add and subtract if we have a common denominator, and we can multiply (remembering to simplify our calculation first, as discussed in Section 1.3) or divide. For an example, we'll perform all these calculations on the fractions $\dfrac{x-2}{x+5}$ and $\dfrac{x-2}{x^2-25}$. Try these calculations yourself, then compare your workings to those in the following table.

A: Addition	B: Subtraction
$\dfrac{x-2}{x+5}+\dfrac{x-2}{x^2-25}\equiv\dfrac{x-2}{x+5}+\dfrac{x-2}{(x-5)(x+5)}$ $\equiv\dfrac{(x-2)(x-5)}{(x+5)(x-5)}+\dfrac{x-2}{(x+5)(x-5)}$ $\equiv\dfrac{(x-2)(x-5)+x-2}{(x+5)(x-5)}$ $\equiv\dfrac{(x-2)(x-5+1)}{(x+5)(x-5)}$ $\equiv\dfrac{(x-2)(x-4)}{(x+5)(x-5)}$	$\dfrac{x-2}{x+5}-\dfrac{x-2}{x^2-25}\equiv\dfrac{x-2}{x+5}-\dfrac{x-2}{(x-5)(x+5)}$ $\equiv\dfrac{(x-2)(x-5)}{(x+5)(x-5)}-\dfrac{x-2}{(x+5)(x-5)}$ $\equiv\dfrac{(x-2)(x-5)-(x-2)}{(x+5)(x-5)}$ $\equiv\dfrac{(x-2)(x-5-1)}{(x+5)(x-5)}$ $\equiv\dfrac{(x-2)(x-6)}{(x+5)(x-5)}$
C: Multiplication	D: Division
$\dfrac{x-2}{x+5}\times\dfrac{x-2}{x^2-25}\equiv\dfrac{x-2}{x+5}\times\dfrac{x-2}{(x-5)(x+5)}$ $\equiv\dfrac{(x-2)^2}{(x-5)(x+5)^2}$	$\dfrac{x-2}{x+5}\div\dfrac{x-2}{x^2-25}\equiv\dfrac{x-2}{x+5}\div\dfrac{x-2}{(x-5)(x+5)}$ $\equiv\dfrac{x-2}{x+5}\times\dfrac{(x-5)(x+5)}{x-2}$ $\equiv\dfrac{x-5}{1}$ $\equiv x-5$

Note, in boxes A and B we employed some clever factorisation on the fourth line of each calculation to simplify the numerator. We needn't have done it like this – we could have expanded the brackets, collected like terms, then factorised the resulting quadratic. But this would not have been as efficient, and one of the lovely things about fluency with techniques is that it leads to efficiency, making laborious procedures less so.

 Thinking about the classroom

Algebraic manipulation can be riddled with misconceptions and common mistakes. You can guarantee you will see students do things like this:

$$(x+4)^2 \equiv x^2 + 16$$
$$(3x)^2 \equiv 3x^2$$
$$\frac{x+2}{x+3} \equiv \frac{2}{3}$$

Think very carefully about why these mistakes happen and how you structure your explanations to minimise them. The first and second examples benefit from being written out longhand as the product of two expressions but, even then, students sometimes fail to see the difference between them: why do we square the 3 and the x in $(3x)^2$ but not simply square the x and the 4 in $(x+4)^2$?

Generally, these mistakes arise from a combination of two things – a lack of fluency in the technique and a lack of understanding of why the technique works. You will see this in the third example where students 'cancel' the x terms because they don't understand the relationships between multiplication, division and the numerator and denominator of a fraction.

 Further exploration

In Section 1.3 we mentioned the **imaginary numbers**. We can use these to factorise the 'sum of two squares', $x^2 + y^2$, which allows us to calculate with **complex numbers**.

There are other algebraic techniques that are essential to more advanced mathematics. 'Partial fractions', for instance, is a technique whereby we write a single fraction as the sum or difference of two others – a bit like 'two fractions were added and here is the answer, what were the two fractions?'. This process is used to make some fractions easier to integrate and differentiate in calculus.

The binomial expansion we met, where we produce potentially long polynomials by expanding repeated brackets, can be taken further to produce infinite series, and the concept of infinite series is integral to trigonometry, calculus and working with complex numbers. For more information on this, look into the Taylor and Maclaurin series.

2.2 Linear equations and inequalities

 Try this first

1 Which method were you taught for solving an equation such as $5x + 2 = 33$? What are the advantages and disadvantages of the method you were taught?

2 Why do we reverse the direction of an **inequality** symbol when we multiply or divide by a negative number?

If manipulating expressions is the grammar of algebra, then equations are the story. With equations we model the world, we work with unknown quantities to explain, make predictions and solve problems. We use them to predict the weather, to model atomic structures, to calculate stresses and strains on buildings, to forecast the stock market, to build cars and much, much more. What we meet in school in early algebra is the very beginnings of almost every branch of mathematics and its subsequent applications.

Setting up an equation is quite simply taking an unknown quantity, assigning a symbol to it and writing down what we know about it. Solving an equation is using this information to find the unknown, and this is where it gets detailed.

Getting the right balance

There are two main approaches to solving an equation: **inverse** operations and balancing. Both have their advantages and disadvantages. Balancing works on the principle that an equation remains true when you apply the same operation to both sides, much like keeping a set of scales in balance.

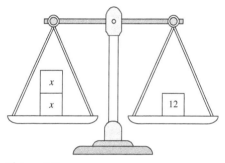

Figure 2.3

The scales analogy is fine when it relates well to the operations involved – we can easily imagine adding or subtracting 2 to both sides and, with a little more effort, doubling or halving both sides. But when things become more abstract, such as 'multiply both sides by x', the image starts to falter. This is a very important consideration with any concrete manipulative or pictorial image in mathematics: we should be methodical in weaning our students off the image, while still applying the lessons it illustrates, so that they can access the abstract without impediment.

Solving an equation by balancing may be approached something like this.

$$5x - 4 = 2x + 1$$
$$5x = 2x + 5 \quad \text{+4 to both sides}$$
$$3x = 5 \quad \text{−2x from both sides}$$
$$x = \frac{5}{3} \quad \text{÷3 on both sides}$$

The alternative to this approach is to think of an equation as a **function machine**, where the unknown is the input. For instance, the equation $12x + 11 = 2$ can be thought of as the function machine shown in Figure 2.4.

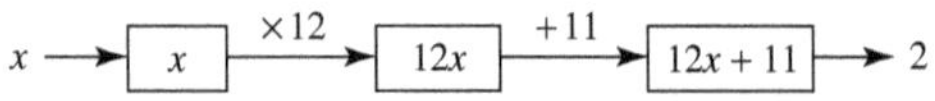

Figure 2.4

To calculate the input we must reverse the function machine, changing each operation for its inverse, as shown in Figure 2.5.

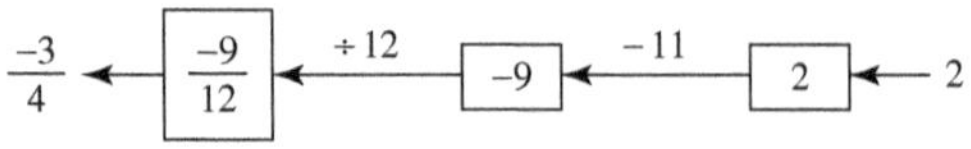

Figure 2.5

Although the process looks identical to balancing, if you see one set of working next to the other, the thinking in the background is a little different. Inverse operations can be particularly effective when faced with a more complex equation. Consider the following.

$$\frac{9\left(2 - \frac{6x}{5}\right)}{7} = 0.1$$

When using the balancing approach it might not be immediately clear to students what to do first. Do I multiply by 7? Divide by 9? Subtract 2? When thinking about the individual operations that are applied to the unknown and *in what order* they are applied, then reversing these operations is clearer. This method also has its limitations though. In equations where the unknown appears twice, it is difficult to think in terms of a flowchart of operations on the unknown. Consider this equation:

$$\frac{x - 5}{2 - 3x} = 6$$

If I ask you what is happening to the unknown, and in what order, your first question is likely to be, 'Which instance of the unknown?'. But once the abstract idea of moving numbers, unknowns, or even entire expressions over the equals sign and inverting, or doing the same to both sides to balance the equation, is mastered, then the image of the flowchart, function machine or balance becomes redundant, and this redundancy is what we guide our students towards.

Discuss

There is no clear best approach to teach students to solve equations. Which method is used in your department? Is everyone aware of the advantages and disadvantages of both? Why might it be important that everyone teaches with the same method?

Equations vs inequalities

We met, in Section 2.1, the identity symbol, $\equiv$, and observed that it is used to show the equivalence between two expressions. Since an equation is true only for *certain* values of the unknown we could never use the identity symbol in the case of equations, only the equals sign. There are times, however, when you want to identify or describe how a relationship holds true for a larger range of values, although still not all values, and these are the times when you solve **inequalities**, which can be expressed through any of the symbols $\leq, \geq, <, >, \neq$. Students can get thrown by inequalities, and it is important to stress that they can be treated just like equations, while taking a little care with the direction of the symbol.

An inequality such as $4 - 3x \geq 10$ can be problematic, and you must avoid the temptation to replace the $\geq$ with $=$. If you do, we have:

$$4 - 3x = 10$$
$$-3x = 6$$
$$x = -\frac{6}{3}$$
$$x = -2$$

and then we replace the $\geq$, getting $x \geq -2$. But if we test a number greater than -2 in the original inequality it does not hold: $4 - 3(0) = 4$, for instance, which is not greater than or equal to 10.

Retaining the inequality symbol in the first place shows where our error occurred:

$4 - 3x \geq 10$ The first two steps remain the same.

$-3x \geq 6$

$-6 \geq 3x$ If we switch each term to the other side here, we see that the unknown is now on the 'smaller' side of the inequality.

$-2 \geq x$ This is the same as $x \leq -2$, which yields numbers that work in the original inequality.

83

So we have an important warning we must give to students when solving inequalities: either they never multiply or divide by a negative number, instead moving the unknown term to the other side to make it positive, or they reverse the inequality symbol when multiplying/dividing by a negative.

To understand why reversing the symbol is necessary, we need to think about the symmetry in the number line. Consider a simple inequality such as $x > 4$. This is shown in the diagram in Figure 2.6, where the hollow circle over 4 shows that this is a *strict inequality,* that is, 4 is not included. (Were the inequality not strict, $x \geq 4$, the circle would be solid.)

Figure 2.6

Now, if we take any number that satisfies this inequality and multiply it by −1, we get the set of numbers shown in Figure 2.7.

Figure 2.7

So we see that if $x > 4$ then $-x < -4$; multiplying by a negative number reverses the inequality symbol in order that the statement remains true.

✎ **2.2 Preparing to teach – do the mathematics!**

Try these questions yourself before proceeding

If $x \geq 2$, $y < -1$ and $0 < z < 1$, write an inequality to represent the following.

1 xy

2 yz

3 $x - y$

4 $\dfrac{x}{z}$

We will consider inequalities in more detail in Section 4.2 but first we need to look at one of the most important things in mathematics: the graph.

2.3 Graphs, linearity and quadratics

> ✅ **Try this first**
>
> **1** What is the purpose of a graph?
>
> **2** Apart from saying, 'it's the slope of a line', how can we define (rather than calculate) the **gradient** of a line?
>
> **3** Why must we write a quadratic equation equal to 0 in order to solve it?

We are getting to the point now where it is hard to decide what to include next – so many concepts begin to dovetail and no one idea is clearly a prerequisite for all others, but with the aim of building our mathematical schema we can't really go any further without looking at graphs. Graphs are key to understanding the relationships between variables and, as such, are essential to mathematical modelling – one of the main applications of mathematics – so it is extremely important to be fluent with equations and graphs.

René Descartes was a philosopher and mathematician in the first half of the seventeenth century. It was he who uttered the now ubiquitous phrase: 'Cogito, ergo sum' ('I think, therefore I am'). We owe much of our algebraic thought to Descartes, who came up with the superscript **index** notation and who decided to use letters at the end of the alphabet for variables (x, y, z) and those at the start for constants (a, b, c). But arguably his most famous legacy is his eponymous one: the Cartesian coordinate system. In 1637, Descartes published *La Géométrie*, which birthed the idea of the axis. It was translated into Latin in 1649 by Frans van Schooten, who added a commentary and popularised the idea of two **orthogonal** (**perpendicular**) axes, splitting the two-dimensional plane into four *quadrants*[2] (and three orthogonal axes to model three dimensions). It was this translation that was picked up by mathematicians such as Newton and Leibniz and which heavily influenced their work in calculus (more on that in Section 4.2).

---

[2] The quadrants are numbered with the first quadrant being where both x and y are positive. Moving anticlockwise from the first quadrant we get the second, third and fourth.

Let's get back to the Cartesian grid. The beauty of this simple idea is that it brings together geometry (favoured by the ancients) and the modern creation of algebra. The Cartesian grid presents a way of visualising a number relationship expressed algebraically. And that is all a graph really is: a picture of a relationship between pairs of numbers.

Take this set of numbers, for instance, assigned the variables x and y.

x	1	2	3	4	5	6
y	−4	−2	0	2	4	6

Looking at these numbers we see some patterns emerge. The values given for the variable x are increasing by 1 each time, but at the same time the values given for y are increasing by 2. We could assume that both variables continue to increase at the same rate – increase x by 1, increase y by 2 – and the Cartesian grid helps us to see this pattern. Plot one variable on the horizontal axis and one on the vertical axis and you get the graph shown in Figure 2.8.

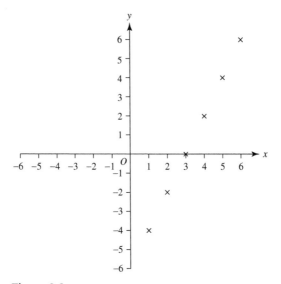

Figure 2.8

The constant rate of increase produces a straight line, and so we call this a *linear* relationship. If we consider successive pairs of (x, y) values (called an *ordered pair*), then we can work out that if we double the x value and subtract 6 then we reach the y value, so x and y are linked by the equation $y = 2x - 6$. This, then, becomes the equation of the line – the line's title, if you like – and we have the start of what we now teach of graphs.

Gradient

Let's consider that graph and its equation again. The gradient of the line is a measure of the slope of the line: steeper lines have a larger gradient. It is quantifiable, measured by considering simultaneously the increase in y and x: for every increase of one in x, the gradient is the corresponding increase or decrease in y.

We can see that, on this graph, for every unit increase in x, y increases by 2, so the gradient of the line is 2. Take two points far apart on the graph and measure the horizontal and vertical distance between them, as shown in Figure 2.9.

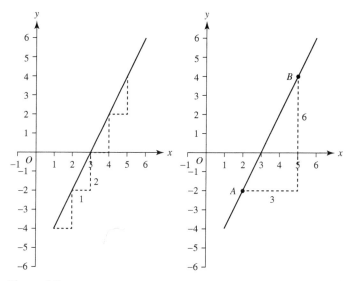

Figure 2.9

Between $A(2, -2)$ and $B(5, 4)$ we see a horizontal increase of 3 and a vertical increase of 6. This still corresponds to 1 across, 2 up, so gives the same measure of the gradient, and shows us how to calculate the gradient of any line: pick two points and divide the vertical distance between them by the horizontal distance.

We write this formula (using the letter m for gradient; no one knows for sure why the letter m was chosen):

$$m = \frac{\Delta y}{\Delta x}$$

where Δ is a Greek capital 'delta', which is very commonly used to mean 'change in' or 'difference in'.

87

From this we see that a line sloping upwards will have a positive gradient, and a line sloping downwards will have a negative gradient. We also see that the gradient is found in the equation of the line and therefore write the general equation of a line as $y = mx + c$, where m is the gradient and c is the y-intercept. How could we prove that c is always the point where the line crosses the y-axis?

The equation of a line needn't be presented in the form $y = mx + c$, but could be any rearrangement of it. Provided the powers of x and y are 1, you have a linear equation. These are all examples of equations that produce straight lines:

$$3y = 1 - 7x$$
$$5y = 8x$$
$$2x + y - 9 = 0$$
$$y - 5 = 3(x - 2)$$

Never forget that the equation of a line is simply the formula that links any x-coordinate with its corresponding y-coordinate and that the line itself is a visual representation of all the pairs of numbers that obey the same rule. Therefore any pair of numbers that satisfies this equation will be coordinates of a point that lies on the line.

Parallel and perpendicular

Clearly parallel lines must have the same gradient; and in a pair of perpendicular lines if one has a positive gradient, then the other has a negative gradient. You will probably know that the gradient of one line is the negative **reciprocal** of the gradient of a perpendicular line (so two lines with gradients $\frac{4}{5}$ and $-\frac{5}{4}$ would be perpendicular). We write this, using m_1 and m_2 for the gradient of each:

$$m_2 = \frac{-1}{m_1} \text{ or } m_1 m_2 = -1$$

Why must this be the case though? Let's take a line with gradient $m_1 = \frac{a}{b}$, so between two points there is a distance of b across and a up. Now rotate the line $90°$ clockwise and observe that the horizontal distance points down and the vertical distance points across, giving us $m_2 = \frac{-b}{a} = -\frac{b}{a}$, which is the negative reciprocal of m_1. Try sketching this for yourself to see the effect.

2.3a Preparing to teach – do the mathematics!

Try this question yourself before proceeding

The line l_1 is perpendicular to the line l_2, which has equation $2x - 3y = 12$. What is the equation of l_1 when the two lines intersect on the x-axis?

 Thinking about the classroom

Students often lack confidence with graphs. From simply mixing up the x- and y-axes, to confusing vertical and horizontal lines of the form $x = n$ and $y = n$, to confusing m and c (which is the gradient and which is the y-intercept?), to being unsure of the shape of different types of curve, and which equations produce which shapes.

Quick decision-making exercises can help to grow students' confidence in all these areas. A decision-making exercise might involve giving students a list of equations and asking them to identify the type of graph they will produce (linear, quadratic, cubic, **exponential**, circle, etc.). It might involve matching sketches of graphs to the equations that could produce them, or it might even be as simple as identifying which linear equations give lines with positive or negative gradient.

Repeated at regular intervals, decision-making exercises allow students to practise what they have learned quickly and without fuss.

Quadratic graphs

The main higher-order equation we meet in school is the quadratic equation. We know that a quadratic equation is of the form $y = ax^2 + bx + c$ and any equation of this form produces a symmetric graph in the shape of a **parabola**, as shown in Figure 2.10.

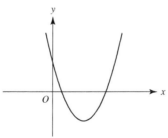

Figure 2.10

Over the page is a table of x- and y-values for the equation $y = x^2$. Clearly the y-coordinates do not grow at the same rate, but increase by increasingly large amounts, which is what produces the curvature in the graph as opposed to a straight line. As the increase in y values grows, the curve gets steeper.

x	−3	−2	−1	0	1	2	3
y	9	4	1	0	1	4	9

In Section 4.2 we will look more specifically at measuring the ever-changing gradient of a curve like this. For now, let's analyse some other parts of the graph. Understanding how to find certain parts of the graph can help when a function is used to model situations. In fact, outside of pure mathematics many functions are used to model physical situations and quadratics are no exception.

Imagine throwing a tennis ball. What shape does the path of the ball take? What about a diver jumping from a diving board, a bullet flying through the air or water spouts from a fountain? They all follow this same path, the shape of which is a parabola. It was Galileo who first experimented and noted that this kind of motion is parabolic, but it wasn't until Newton came along with his Laws of Motion that we had a formal mathematical model. Start by considering movement with no acceleration, in which case we know that speed $= \dfrac{\text{distance}}{\text{time}}$. Now introduce some constant acceleration ('constant' having the usual mathematical meaning here of 'unchanging'), which means the start and end speeds for any section of a journey are different, and we have the formula average speed $= \dfrac{\text{distance}}{\text{time}}$.

We use the letters u and v for initial and final velocity, respectively (v for velocity is obvious; u is chosen since it is close to v in the alphabet and is representing the same idea). To confuse things a little we call our distance travelled s (this comes from the Latin *spatium*, meaning distance or space), but we stick with t for time. The formula is:

$$\frac{u+v}{2} = \frac{s}{t}$$

We can generate a second equation using the fact that acceleration (a) is the change in speed per unit of time, giving us:

$$a = \frac{v-u}{t}$$

Now, we combine these two equations and do some rearranging (have a go at this yourself) to get the beautifully useful equation:

$$s = ut + \frac{1}{2}at^2$$

This lovely model uses the initial speed of an object (u), the time of travel (t) and the acceleration (a) to calculate how far it will go. Notice the powers of t: this is a quadratic equation.

We can take the idea further to help us model our tennis balls and divers, which we call projectiles. Projectile motion can be considered as two-dimensional (things move horizontally and vertically at the same time). Using these equations and some trigonometry of right-angled triangles we model the motion in both directions. We need to know that the acceleration of projectiles is due to gravity, which pulls vertically downwards towards the centre of the Earth at approximately 9.8 m/s². This never changes, so we can stick with our initial premise that acceleration is constant. We use the letter g for this acceleration due to gravity, and g takes different values on different planets, which is why the lunar explorers of the twentieth century looked like they couldn't quite keep their feet on the ground. The quadratic equation that models any projectile (given its angle of projection, α, and initial velocity, u) is:

$$y = x \tan \alpha - \frac{gx^2}{2u^2 \cos^2 \alpha}$$

For different values of α and u you can draw the graph of this equation, which is precisely the path the flying object will follow through the air.

Quadratic equations

Factorising

We can find any point on a graph by substituting one of its coordinates into the equation and solving to find the other. Curves come with complexities not present with straight lines, though. Let's work with the equation of $y = x^2 - 9x + 20$ and assume we want to find out where the graph has a y-coordinate of 12. There are two such places shown on the diagram in Figure 2.11 and we can find them by substituting 12 for y in the equation, giving $x^2 - 9x + 20 = 12$.

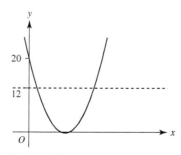

Figure 2.11

In theory, we could solve this by factorising the equation to give $(x-5)(x-4) = 12$. This means we are looking for two numbers whose product is 12, one of which is 5 less than a fixed number (x) and the other of which is 4 less than the same number. You *could* find these numbers, but you'd have to have either a quick flash of inspiration or you'd have to plough through a lot of possibilities. Considering integers alone, 12 has three pairs of factors, but we don't necessarily know whether or not the solutions are integers.

What we can do, however, is transform this equation to another one that is quite straightforward to solve. Let's subtract 12 from both sides of the equation to get $x^2 - 9x + 8 = 0$. Graphically we have translated the original parabola down by 12 units so that the points of the x-coordinate we are trying to find lie on the x-axis. This new equation can be solved by factorising, with the bonus that if the product of two numbers is 0, one of those numbers *must* be 0. Hence we have:

$$x^2 - 9x + 8 = 0$$
$$(x-8)(x-1) = 0$$
$$x - 8 = 0 \text{ or } x - 1 = 0$$
$$x = 8 \text{ or } x = 1$$

(Notice how these x values solve the original equation of $x^2 - 9x + 20 = 12$, too.) So it is not that we *cannot* solve a quadratic equation if it is not equal to 0, but it is not straightforward.

These x values, where a quadratic graph crosses the x-axis, are called the **roots** of the equation. There are more quadratic equations with irrational roots than there are with rational roots, so factorising is not always the best way of solving a quadratic equation.

Completing the square

Let's remind ourselves of a particularly useful technique for analysing quadratic functions: **completing the square**. Consider some blocks, as in Figure 2.12 – two squares and two identical rectangles – where the large square has dimensions $x \times x$, the rectangles have dimensions $x \times 1$ and $1 \times x$, and the small square has dimensions 1×1.

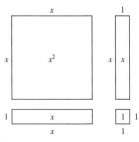

Figure 2.12

If we place some of these blocks in the arrangement shown in Figure 2.13, we create a square with side length $x+3$ and area $(x+3)^2$ or x^2+6x+9.

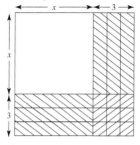

Figure 2.13

Note that to make a perfect square the side length must be $x+\dfrac{b}{2}$ (where b is the coefficient of x in the expanded quadratic) and the number of small squares in the bottom right corner is the square of this halved coefficient. In our example, $b=6$, which makes the side length $x+3$ and gives nine small squares in the bottom right corner.

We can also represent the quadratic x^2+6x+4 using these blocks, getting as close to a perfect square in shape as we can, as shown in Figure 2.14.

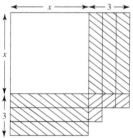

Figure 2.14

In doing this we can see that this quadratic expression is five small blocks short of the perfect square, so we can write it as $(x+3)^2-5$, thinking of this as the square with side length $x+3$ but with five small squares removed from the bottom right. This is the process of completing the square – seeing how a given quadratic varies from a perfect square.

 Thinking about the classroom

The image of completing the square shown here can be used in the classroom with algebra tiles, which can be bought as physical manipulatives or displayed onscreen. Algebra tiles are one of a number of concrete manipulatives, including Dienes blocks and Cuisenaire rods, which can help students to make sense of abstract mathematical ideas.

The visualisation we have seen here works beautifully when all the terms in the quadratic are positive, but needs some tweaking (and a leap of imagination) when there are negative terms. As with the other pictorial representations we have seen, such as balancing scales in Section 2.2, once the mathematical principles are sufficiently practised we can move students on to applying the technique abstractly.

Let's now compare the completed square form of a quadratic to the graph of the quadratic, continuing with $y = x^2 + 6x + 4 = (x+3)^2 - 5$.

The completed square form shows us that this quadratic is a translation of $y = x^2$ by the vector $\begin{pmatrix} -3 \\ -5 \end{pmatrix}$ (we will look at translating graphs properly in Section 4.2) and so the coordinates of the minimum point are $(-3, -5)$. We can use this form to find the roots of the equation, too.

$$(x+3)^2 - 5 = 0$$
$$(x+3)^2 = 5$$
$$x+3 = \pm\sqrt{5}$$
$$x = -3 \pm \sqrt{5}$$

The graph of the quadratic is shown in Figure 2.15.

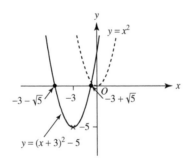

Figure 2.15

The quadratic formula

In fact, completing the square leads us to the universally infamous method of solving a quadratic equation: the quadratic formula (known in some parts of Germany and Switzerland as mitternachtsformel, or midnight formula, for the fact that you learn it so well you could recite it at midnight when half asleep). The general solution to a quadratic equation was known by Indian mathematician Brahmagupta in the seventh century but was first described in words by the Flemish mathematician Simon Stevin (he of decimalisation in Section 1.3) in his 1585 work *Arithmetic*; the equation appears in the form we now know in none other than *La Géométrie* by Descartes. Let us take the general quadratic equation $ax^2 + bx + c = 0$ and complete the square.

$x^2 + \dfrac{b}{a}x + \dfrac{c}{a} = 0$	Divide the whole equation by a to make the leading coefficient 1.
$\left(x + \dfrac{b}{2a}\right)^2 - \left(\dfrac{b}{2a}\right)^2 + \dfrac{c}{a} = 0$	Complete the square. (Note we have halved the coefficient of x and subtracted the square of this.)
$\left(x + \dfrac{b}{2a}\right)^2 - \dfrac{b^2}{4a^2} + \dfrac{4ac}{4a^2} = 0$	The second and third fractions on the left-hand side now have a common denominator.
$\left(x + \dfrac{b}{2a}\right)^2 = \dfrac{b^2 - 4ac}{4a^2}$	Move the two fractions with a common denominator to the other side of the equation and combine with subtraction.
$x + \dfrac{b}{2a} = \pm\sqrt{\dfrac{b^2 - 4ac}{4a^2}}$	Take the square root of both sides.
$x = -\dfrac{b}{2a} \pm \dfrac{\sqrt{b^2 - 4ac}}{2a}$	Rearrange to make x the subject, while applying the square root to the numerator and denominator of the fraction.
$x = \dfrac{-b \pm \sqrt{b^2 - 4ac}}{2a}$	Combine into a single fraction.

Mathematicians have wanted to find the general solution to higher-order polynomials for centuries. Gerolamo Cardano found a method for solving the cubic $ax^3 + bx^2 + cx + d = 0$, published in his 1545 work *Ars Magna*, and others have found alternatives over the years.[3] The 'cubic formula' is not one you would ever want to memorise, and the formula for a quartic ($ax^4 + \dots$) would take more than a page of this book to write out in full. It is often the case that some kind of iterative approach is most useful for solving higher-order polynomial equations, as we will see in Section 4.2.

 2.3b Preparing to teach – do the mathematics!

Try this question yourself before proceeding

Using the quadratic formula, demonstrate that in any quadratic either both roots are rational or both are irrational (but that it is impossible to have one rational and one irrational root).

---

[3] This, as with a number of events in mathematical history, was not without its controversy. Cardano is said to have learnt the method from fellow Italian Niccolo Fontana Tartaglia, who made Cardano promise not to publish the result. Cardano did not keep his promise and the two entered into a lifelong feud.

More on roots

What else can we know about quadratics? Well, let's imagine a quadratic equation $ax^2 + bx + c = 0$, which can be rewritten $x^2 + \dfrac{b}{a}x + \dfrac{c}{a} = 0$, has two **real** roots, call them α and β,[4] then it must be the case that $(x - \alpha)(x - \beta) = 0$. Expanding this gives $x^2 - \alpha x - \beta x + \alpha\beta = 0$ or $x^2 - (\alpha + \beta)x + \alpha\beta = 0$. Comparing the coefficients of x and x^0 in these two equations tells us that the product of the roots of a quadratic equation, $\alpha\beta$, is equal to $\dfrac{c}{a}$ and their sum, $\alpha + \beta$, is equal to $-\dfrac{b}{a}$. This gives you a handy way to check your solutions to a quadratic equation: do they sum to $-\dfrac{b}{a}$? Is their product $\dfrac{c}{a}$?

We also have a way of knowing whether or not a quadratic equation has real roots. We use the **discriminant** of the quadratic equation, $b^2 - 4ac$, so called because it discriminates between types of quadratic. Note this is the part inside the square root in the quadratic formula, which is what makes it important. There are no real square roots of a negative number, so if $b^2 - 4ac < 0$ then the quadratic has no real solutions (and its graph does not cross the x-axis). If $b^2 - 4ac > 0$ there are two real solutions, since any positive number has two real square roots: the positive and the negative. And if $b^2 - 4ac = 0$ there is one repeated root, as the square root part of the formula disappears. Other

---

 Further exploration

The fundamental theorem of algebra tells us that any polynomial of degree n with **complex** coefficients has n roots, so a quadratic has two roots, a cubic three, a quintic five, and so on. These roots may not all be real (some may have imaginary parts) and some may be repeated, as in the case of $x^2 = 0$, where the root of 0 is repeated twice (we say it has **multiplicity** 2). There are interesting results and patterns that arise in the case of complex roots.

Abel's impossibility theorem from 1824 proves that there can be no general formula (like the quadratic formula) for any polynomial of degree 5 or higher. As with many seemingly simple results in mathematics, the proof of this requires much more advanced mathematics than the result itself.

---

[4] Why do we use Greek letters? You might answer simply 'why not?'. But facetiousness aside, there is a good reason for it. We have already seen that Descartes conventionalised using letters at the end of the alphabet for variables and those at the start for constants. Here we are dealing with constants, but the letters a, b and c already have a very specific meaning in this context, so jumping to another alphabet makes sense. Since the Greeks are the forefathers of much of our mathematical thought, and Greek has been widespread throughout the Western world for two millennia, it became the obvious choice. Greek letters are particularly used in geometry for labelling angles.

polynomial equations also have discriminants that tell you information about the number and type of roots, but these discriminants quickly get complex.

Beware losing solutions

Have a go at solving the equation

$$4(x+2) = 4(3x-8)$$

Did you start by dividing both sides by 4, leaving $x+2 = 3x-8$? That would certainly simplify the equation quickly. Now have a go at solving

$$x(x+2) = x(3x-8)$$

Did you start by dividing both sides by x, just as with the linear equation above? If you did, you would have had the same solution as before, $x = 5$. But this is problematic because the original equation is a quadratic equation, not a linear one, and so we would expect two roots. Where has the other root gone?

The error came when dividing by x. In dividing the whole equation by a variable we have reduced the order of the equation – a quadratic with two solutions has become a linear with one solution. Instead, to solve this equation we must expand and rearrange.

$$x^2 + 2x = 3x^2 - 8x$$
$$2x^2 - 10x = 0$$
$$2x(x-5) = 0$$
$$x = 0 \text{ or } x = 5$$

Note the lost solution was 0. If you can ever divide your whole equation by a variable and eliminate it, then one of the solutions must have been 0. Dividing by 0 is an interesting concept; we will revisit it in Sections 4.2 and 4.3.

Transcendental and algebraic numbers

One of the wonderful things about mathematics is the way ideas can start off simply and be extended without end. In the classroom we can always stretch our students if we know how to go deeper into the topic of study; this is one of the reasons why it is so very important to enhance our own subject knowledge. There are some parts of mathematics we may never use in the classroom, but knowing them enriches our own mathematical schema, helping us to appreciate aspects of our subject in a different way.

The solutions to polynomial equations are no exception. Polynomial equations introduce us to a different way of categorising the **real numbers**: *algebraic* and *transcendental* numbers. Algebraic numbers are those that can be the root of a polynomial equation with integer coefficients. Those that *cannot* be are called *transcendental,* as they transcend algebra. The numbers π and e are two such numbers: there are no polynomial equations with integer coefficients that have either as roots.

Transcendental numbers are always irrational, but not all irrational numbers are transcendental (the solutions to $x^2 - 5 = 0$, for instance, are the two algebraic irrational numbers $\pm\sqrt{5}$). It is very hard to show that a number is transcendental, even if it is composed of transcendental numbers. Take πe, $\frac{\pi}{e}$, π+e and π−e for instance: we do not know if these are transcendental or algebraic (in fact we do not know if they are even irrational). In terms of mathematical history, transcendental numbers are a relatively recent discovery. Euler first started to consider the idea in the 1740s, but it wasn't until the 1840s, when Frenchman Joseph Liouville found and proved some numbers transcendental, that anyone knew they really existed. Liouville's constant is the number 0.110 001 000 000 000 000 000 001... , which has a 1 in each position after the decimal point that is a factorial (the 1!th position, the 2!th position, etc.) and 0s everywhere else.[5] Liouville discovered his transcendental numbers by working with **continued fractions** (see Section 1.3). Irrational numbers have infinite continuous fraction representations; Liouville's constant starts:

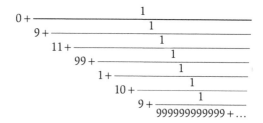

The **partial denominators** continue to get large and exhibit no pattern.

Continued fractions crop up in all sorts of places. We mentioned earlier that all irrational numbers have infinite continued fraction representations. Many of these have no pattern, as we saw with Liouville's constant. However, there is one set of irrational numbers, namely, the *quadratic irrationals,* that are particularly interesting. Quadratic irrationals are those irrational numbers that are the roots of a quadratic equation with integer coefficients, and their continued fraction representations are the only ones that are periodic (that is, the partial denominators follow a repeating pattern). Consider $\sqrt{3}$, whose

---

[5] *n*! is read 'n *factorial*' and is the function that takes the product of *n* and every integer less than it, down to 1. So 1! = 1, 2! = 2 × 1 = 2, 3! = 3 × 2 × 1 = 6, 4! = 4 × 3 × 2 × 1 = 24, and so on.

continued fraction representation is:

$$\sqrt{3} = 1 + \cfrac{1}{1 + \cfrac{1}{2 + \cfrac{1}{1 + \cfrac{1}{2 + \cfrac{1}{1 + \ldots}}}}}$$

It is quite astounding that irrational numbers, whose decimal representations display no pattern, can have other representations that are entirely predictable!

2.4 Simultaneous equations

✅ **Try this first**

1 What situations give rise to simultaneous equations?

2 How do we know how many solutions simultaneous equations have?

3 How many techniques do you know for solving simultaneous equations?

Out in the big, wide, mathematical world, equations very rarely consist of one variable. The weather, for instance, doesn't depend on only the air temperature; a factory doesn't necessarily make only one product; and the world is seen in three dimensions, not one. Very often, systems of equations involve multiple variables, and this is why we need to be able to solve simultaneous equations.

The equation $y = 2x - 1$ has infinitely many pairs of solutions which, when graphed, lie on a straight line, just as the infinitely many pairs of solutions to the equation $y = 6 - x$ do. There is only one pair of values that satisfies both equations, however, and this represents the point where the two lines intersect, shown in Figure 2.16.

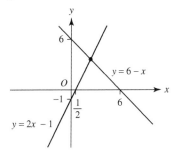

Figure 2.16

How many pairs of values simultaneously solve the equations $y = 2x - 1$ and $y = x^2 - 3x$? If we sketch the graphs (see Figure 2.17) we can see the answer and estimate the solutions, but to calculate them we need to do some **substitution**.

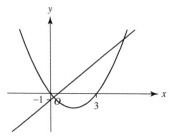

Figure 2.17

Knowing that $y = 2x - 1$, substitute $2x - 1$ for y in the quadratic:

$$2x - 1 = x^2 - 3x$$
$$x^2 - 5x + 1 = 0$$
$$x = \frac{5 \pm \sqrt{21}}{2}$$

To find the corresponding y values we can substitute the x values into either of the original equations, but clearly the linear one is more straightforward. When $x = \dfrac{5 + \sqrt{21}}{2}$, $y = 2\left(\dfrac{5 + \sqrt{21}}{2}\right) - 1 = 4 + \sqrt{21}$ and when $x = \dfrac{5 - \sqrt{21}}{2}$, $y = 2\left(\dfrac{5 - \sqrt{21}}{2}\right) - 1 = 4 - \sqrt{21}$.

 2.4 Preparing to teach – do the mathematics!

Try these questions yourself before proceeding

1 If a pair of linear simultaneous equations has no solutions, what can you say about their graphical representation?

2 Not every straight line will cross a quadratic in two places. Some of them will be **tangential**, so there will be only one solution, and some of them will not meet the curve at all. How many points of intersection could a line and a cubic have? How about two quadratics? A quadratic and a cubic? An mth and nth degree polynomial?

The method of solving simultaneous equations we have just used is called substitution. Often it is the best way to solve simultaneous equations, but in the case where rearranging for y produces a complicated expression, **elimination** can be better. Take the simultaneous equations $2x + 2y = 5$ and $3x - y = 5$. Making y or x the subject of either and substituting would create a lot of work. Elimination, the first technique we tend to teach in school, is superior in the case of two linear equations like this, although not for most other cases.

$$2x + 2y = 5 \Rightarrow 6x + 6y = 15 \text{ (1)}$$
$$3x - y = 5 \Rightarrow 6x - 2y = 10 \text{ (2)}$$

Subtracting equation (2) from equation (1) gives $8y = 5$, so $y = \dfrac{5}{8}$. Substituting this into the second untransformed equation gives $3x - \dfrac{5}{8} = 5$, so $x = \dfrac{15}{8}$. The solution we have arrived at can be verified by substituting the x and y values into the first equation, giving $2\left(\dfrac{15}{8}\right) + 2\left(\dfrac{5}{8}\right) = 5$.

 Thinking about the classroom

There are so many places that students make mistakes with this process: deciding whether to add or subtract the equations, adding or subtracting negative terms incorrectly, substituting the first solution incorrectly. As with any multistep process, spend time in the classroom practising each step carefully to reduce the chances of error.

 Further exploration

Simultaneous equations appear throughout mathematics, and there may be more than two variables. As we increase the number of unknowns in a system of linear equations, it becomes cumbersome to solve them using elimination or substitution. We turn, instead, to matrices, where we can use one of two methods: inverse matrices or row reduction (which is, in essence, systematic elimination).

Quiz 2

1. Expand and simplify $(x + 2y - 3z)(x + 2y + 3z)$.

2. Expand and simplify $(2m - n)(m + 2n)(2m + n)(m - 2n)$.

3. Factorise $8y^4 - 13y^2 - 6$.

4. The product of the roots of the quadratic equation $ax^2 + bx + 40 = 0$ is 8 and the midpoint of the roots is 5.4. Find the values of a and b, given that they are both integers.

5. The fraction $\dfrac{x}{y}$ is equivalent to 10. When I add 5 to the numerator, the new fraction is equivalent to 11. What are the values of x and y?

6. Solve the equation $\dfrac{2x - 6}{3} + \dfrac{x}{10} - \dfrac{1 - 6x}{4} = 2$.

7. To find the point(s) of intersection of the curve $y = \sqrt{x}$ and the line $y = 2x - 6$, we could solve the equation $\sqrt{x} = 2x - 6$ like this:

$$x = (2x - 6)^2 = 4x^2 - 24x + 36$$
$$4x^2 - 25x + 36 = 0$$
$$(4x - 9)(x - 4) = 0$$

From this we get $x = 4$ or $x = \dfrac{9}{4}$ and can find the corresponding y-coordinates. Which of these solutions are valid and why?

8. Simplify the expression $\dfrac{x^2 - 6x}{2x - 1} \div \dfrac{x - 6}{5} + \dfrac{4x}{1 - 2x}$.

9. The line l_1 has equation $6y = 9x + 16$ and a perpendicular line l_2 has y-intercept at most double the y-intercept of l_1. What can you infer about the x-intercept of l_2?

10. When is it true that $(x + y)^2 = x^2 + y^2$?

11. Write down the decision process you would go through (and would show to students) to decide how to solve any given quadratic equation.

12. When is the square root of a number greater than the number itself?

Answers to each Quiz, Try this first *and* Preparing to teach *are at the back of the book.*

Chapter 3

Number II: Multiplicative thinking

3.1 Scaling and proportional thinking

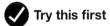 **Try this first**

1 How many ways can you represent 2×6 in a diagram? How many of these work for $\frac{1}{2} \times 6$ or -2×6?

2 Why is -2×-5 equal to 10?

3 When making a meal for 6 people using a recipe for 4, why can you not add 2 to all the ingredients?

Multiplication with rational numbers

Multiplication is one of the most important concepts we teach; it is difficult to think of any area of mathematics that is not built upon it in some way. In the classroom, we tend to think of multiplication as repeated addition, for example, 5×2 is five lots of two, or $2 + 2 + 2 + 2 + 2$. In Section 2.1 we considered this idea when we looked at algebra as a generalisation of number. But repeated addition can be problematic. Thinking of 4×3 as $3 + 3 + 3 + 3$, or even as $4 + 4 + 4$, is useful as an inroad to multiplying, but we should not limit multiplication to this.

How does the idea of repeated addition work when we are using negative numbers? For -3×4, how can I 'add four, minus three times'? Perhaps in this instance we must employ **commutativity** to make sense, so 'add minus three four times' gives $-3 + -3 + -3 + -3$, which is easier to comprehend. Make the calculation -3×-4 and we can't even force a repeated addition through commutativity: 'add minus four, minus three times' makes as little sense as 'add minus three, minus four times'.

How does the idea of repeated addition work when we have fractions? You cannot think of $\frac{1}{2} \times 8$ as 'add eight, one half times'. Commutativity works here – 'add one half, eight times' is conceivable. But if we move on to something like $\frac{1}{2} \times \frac{3}{4}$ we have the same nonsensical problem as with negatives, both 'add three quarters, one half times' and 'add one half, three quarters times' do nothing but muddy the waters.

The repeated addition model also struggles when we come to think of division as the **inverse** of multiplication. Is division repeated subtraction? Certainly to calculate $12 \div 4$ we could repeatedly subtract 4 until we reach 0 and see that this happens three times: $12 - 4 - 4 - 4$ but this model is all but useless if we want to calculate $12 \div -4$ and doesn't contribute much to an understanding of division.

So repeated addition (and its inverse, repeated subtraction) is hugely limiting. It is important, therefore, that we convey a stronger model of multiplication to our students, that of multiplication as scaling or stretching. This is the idea that underpins **proportional** reasoning.

Let's take 4×3 again and consider a line of length 4. Multiplying it by 3 is akin to stretching the line until it is three times as long, so of length 12. The scaling image is particularly strong when you take the **integers** from 0 to 5 and multiply them all by 3: the **products**, marked on a number line as in Figure 3.1, convey the stretching out that multiplication achieves.

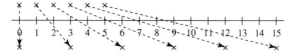

Figure 3.1

If we think of multiplication as the size of the stretch, then we can see from Figure 3.1 that 1 is to 3 as 2 is to 6, or as 10 is to 30. All pairs of numbers connected by the arrows are linked by the same relationship, that of multiplication by 3.

This new picture of scaling copes quite well with **multiplicands** between 0 and 1, where the stretch becomes more of a squash. $5 \times \frac{1}{2}$ can be pictured as a line of length 5 that is then squashed to half the length. All the numbers from 1 to 10 multiplied by $\frac{1}{2}$ can be seen on the number line in Figure 3.2.

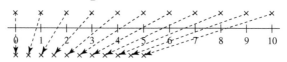

Figure 3.2

It is particularly important, when dealing with multiplication, to convey the principle that the numbers between 0 and 1 have the opposite effect to the numbers over 1. So $\times 3$ will stretch by a factor of 3, whereas $\times \frac{1}{3}$ will squash by a factor of 3, just as $\times \frac{8}{5}$ will stretch by a factor of $\frac{8}{5}$ (or 1.6), whereas $\times \frac{5}{8}$ will squash by a factor of $\frac{8}{5}$ (or 1.6). This reinforces the relationship between **reciprocals** and the **multiplicative identity**, 1, and is something many students grapple with, especially when they are so used to seeing multiplication produce a result larger than either of the numbers being multiplied.

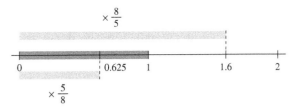

Figure 3.3 A line of length 1 scaled by $\frac{8}{5}$ and its reciprocal, $\frac{5}{8}$

An infinite aside

The concept of numbers greater than 1 being the opposite (in a multiplicative sense) of numbers between 0 and 1 is quite fascinating and leads us to think about infinity in ways that can be counter-intuitive. Stop and consider, for a moment, that every single **real number** greater than 1 – every single one – has a reciprocal between 0 and 1. That suggests to us that the numbers between 0 and 1 are denser than those above 1, but this is not quite the case.

In fact, the mind-blowing thing about the real number line is that there are as many real numbers in a given interval on the line as there are *on the whole line*; so there are as many numbers between 0 and 1 as there are along the whole real number line, or there are as many numbers between 0 and 10 as there are between 0 and 1. This is thanks to the scaling nature of multiplication (and division). We could take every real number between 0 and 10 and divide it by 10, producing every real number between 0 and 1. We say there are c numbers in any interval of real numbers and c is called the *cardinality* (or size) of the set of real numbers.

We owe this crazy idea to Georg Cantor, a German mathematician born in 1845. Cantor developed set theory and was the first mathematician to consider different types of infinity. 'Different types of infinity' sounds rather bizarre, but not all infinities are the same size. The **natural numbers**, integers and **rational numbers** are what we call 'countably infinite'. The cardinality, or size, of their infinity is called $\aleph_0$ (aleph-naught, which uses the Hebrew letter aleph[1]). To understand this idea, let's consider some finite sets first. The set $\{2, 3, 4\}$ has cardinality 3, as there are three elements in the set. Any other set with three elements has the same cardinality, and we demonstrate that two sets have the same cardinality if we can map every element from one set onto a unique element in the other. So, for instance, the set $\{2, 3, 4\}$ can be mapped to the set $\{6, 8, 10\}$, as shown below. (This mapping could equally be reversed.)

$$2 \rightarrow 6$$
$$3 \rightarrow 8$$
$$4 \rightarrow 10$$

This mapping is called a bijection, and we use this to show how some infinite sets of numbers have the same cardinality.

The set of natural numbers $\{1, 2, 3, 4, ...\}$ is pretty much the definition of 'countably infinite': we can count them and continue to infinity. You might be tempted to think that the set of even numbers, $\{2, 4, 6, 8, ...\}$ is smaller than the set of natural numbers – perhaps there are half as many – but that would be a mistake. There exists a bijection from the set of natural numbers to the set of even numbers:

$$1 \rightarrow 2$$
$$2 \rightarrow 4$$
$$3 \rightarrow 6$$

and this bijection means the two sets have the same cardinality, $\aleph_0$. So, there are as many even numbers as there are natural numbers. We can do the same thing with integers:

$$1 \rightarrow 0$$
$$2 \rightarrow 1$$
$$3 \rightarrow -1$$
$$4 \rightarrow 2$$
$$5 \rightarrow -2$$
$$6 \rightarrow 3$$

meaning they also have cardinality $\aleph_0$.

---

[1] In one of those rare occasions in mathematics where neither the Latin nor Greek alphabets sufficed, Cantor turned to Hebrew, quite possibly because of his Jewish background. It has been speculated that this letter was particularly apt as it is the first letter in the Hebrew word *ein-sof*, meaning *infinity*.

Further exploration

Cantor developed a lovely demonstration of how we can create a bijection from the natural numbers to the rationals and his *diagonal proof*, showing that the same cannot be done for the irrationals, is extremely important. When looking into Cantor's set theory and the cardinality of the real numbers, take some time to consider the concept of the *power set* and what relevance it has to the cardinality of the real numbers.

It can be shown that the rational numbers are also countably infinite, but that the irrationals (and, hence, the real numbers) are uncountably infinite, so have bigger cardinality.

Back to negatives

When applying scaling to multiplication (or division) by negatives, there are only two ideas to master. The first is the **magnitude** of the scale: $\times 4$ makes something four times as big, so -3×4 can mean 'stretch -3 out four times its length', as in Figure 3.4.

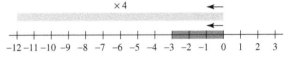

Figure 3.4

The second is the direction of the scale: a negative forces us to move in the opposite direction. Imagine a reflection in a vertical line through 0 where -4×-3 takes -3, scales it by 4 to -12, then reflects in this invisible line to give 12, as in Figure 3.5.

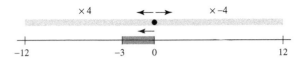

Figure 3.5

The idea of negative multiplication producing a reflection links with reflecting **functions**, which we will meet in Section 4.2, and the effects of a negative enlargement. It is useful when considering a longer calculation: every time you see a negative sign, you alternate between positive and negative. Something like $5 \times -3 \times -4 \times 2 \times -1$ can be evaluated by finding the magnitude of the product (but ignoring its sign), then considering subsequent negatives as alternating between negative and positive. Here, three negative signs have the effect of negative–positive–negative and the answer will be –120. What students can struggle to understand at first is that the calculation $-5 \times 3 \times -4 \times -2 \times 1$ would produce exactly the same answer.

 Thinking about the classroom

We mentioned manipulatives when talking about completing the square. Some teachers use negative tiles to help teach operations with negative numbers. In Singapore, for instance, these tiles are advocated centrally and used everywhere.

Each tile has 1 on one side and –1 on the reverse. A calculation such as 4×3 can be set up with twelve tiles in a rectangular array, positive side up. When changed to -4×3 all the four rows of tiles are flipped over, showing twelve negative faces. If the calculation then becomes -4×-3, the three columns are flipped again to show twelve positive faces.

This conveys the same idea as we have considered here – that multiplication by a negative number reflects a solution about zero, changing its sign.

 Discuss

Which methods do you use to teach multiplication and division by negative numbers? Do you use a number line? Is it horizontal or vertical? What problems do your students face and how do you systematically address them?

Proportional reasoning

Scaling helps us to consider the relationships between the numbers in multiplication in a new way. Starting with the multiplicative identity, 1, we can consider 3×4, as in Figure 3.6.

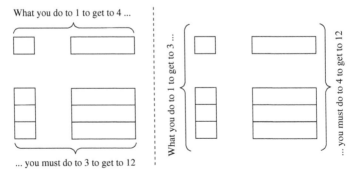

Figure 3.6

This allows us to access proportional reasoning, the idea that multiplication represents quantities changing in direct proportion with one another: when one doubles, so does the other, and when one halves, so does the other.

This is the thinking that underpins recipes – for instance, if 2 eggs are needed for a Victoria sponge cake that will serve 8 people, then 4 eggs are needed for a sponge that will serve 16 people: what you do to 8 to get 16, you must do to 2 to get 4. In Figure 3.7, a similar diagram to the previous one highlights the multiplicative relationships in this one culinary delight.

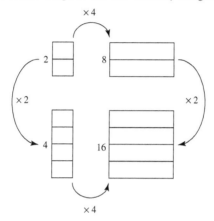

Figure 3.7

This same thinking underpins calculations of a 'value for money' nature. If I can buy 12.5 kg of potatoes for £4.94, or 8 kg for £3.20, which is the better value?

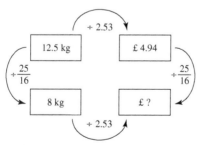

Figure 3.8

The calculations here would make the 8 kg bag cost £3.16, which means the actual price of £3.20 makes this bag worse value for money. It is worth pointing out, at this stage, that a unitary method – finding the price for 1 kg – is the intuitive approach for many students. Here they would have the 12.5 kg bag at £0.3952 per kg and the 8 kg bag at £0.40 per kg, but it is not uncommon for students to divide the wrong way and draw the wrong conclusion, say $4.94 \div 12.5 = 2.53$ £ per kg, instead of kg per £. Getting them to put the 'units' with their answer can help to mitigate this problem.

 3.1a Preparing to teach – do the mathematics!

Try these questions yourself before proceeding

1. A new car has an average fuel efficiency of 40 kilometres per litre (km/l). Two of these cars travel a journey together. The cars stop for a break after they have travelled $\frac{2}{3}$ of the way. If, at this point, they have used two litres of fuel between them, estimate the length of the journey.

2. A builder and his apprentice are building fixed-size walls. The builder could build a wall alone in 4 hours. His apprentice is half as quick. Assuming they each work at a constant rate, how long does it take them to build two walls together?

There are plenty of students who will try to add and subtract in proportional reasoning situations because they do not understand that multiplication and division underlie this reasoning, and it is not always apparent to students that any combination of multiplication and division will maintain a proportional relationship. For instance, a recipe for 10 people can be scaled to cook for 12 people, but we don't have to multiply by 1.2; we could divide by 5 and multiply by 6 instead. This may seem very obvious to you, but many ideas that are obvious to us are not clear to our students. One of our responsibilities is to make explicit the things we take for granted and allow students to practise them until they become obvious to them, too.

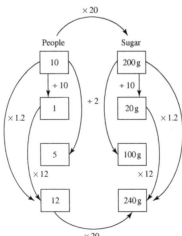

Figure 3.9 Some possible routes from 10 to 12 (and from 200 to 240)

We will revisit proportional thinking in Section 3.3 when we move to more abstract algebraic ideas.

Percentages

'Per cent' means 'out of 100' and comes from the Latin *per centum*. The % symbol has evolved over the past six hundred or so years, as the abbreviation 'p100' morphed with a fraction bar, eventually becoming %.

Percentages are the ultimate leveller, taking a number line from 0 to any number and scaling it to fit the number line from 0 to 100, as in Figure 3.10.

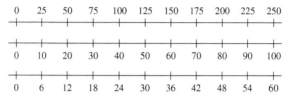

Figure 3.10

Often taught with fractions and decimals as another way of representing parts of a whole, percentages can become separated from the proportional reasoning that underlies them, and this is normally why students make mistakes with them. There are plenty of times you will hear something like, 'To find 10% you divide by 10 so to find 20% you divide by 20'. Just as a fraction wall is helpful to visualise equivalent fractions, so a bar model of some kind can help to visualise percentages.

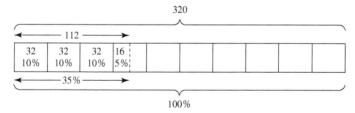

Figure 3.11

The unitary method, or finding 1%, is one way of minimising the risk of students mixing up when to multiply, when to divide, and what to multiply or divide by. More complex problems can be made simple with this method, especially when combined with a suitable visual aid.

For instance, suppose one year there were record falls in house prices, with the average depreciation being 16% in a year. For one house in a street this might represent a drop in price of £45 000. How much did the house cost before the crash? Setting up a bar model here requires us to assign the

111

correct numbers to the correct sections of the bar, but in so doing we are able to see very clearly what resulting calculations are needed.

Figure 3.12

From Figure 3.12 we see that $16\% = £45\,000$, so $1\% = \dfrac{45\,000}{16} = £2812.50$ and therefore $100\% = 2812.5 \times 100 = £281\,250$.

In the same crash, another house on the street might have fallen to £252 840. How much did it cost before the crash?

Figure 3.13

We can see that £252 840 represents 84% of the original value, so $1\% = \dfrac{252\,840}{84} = £3010$ and $100\% = 3010 \times 100 = £301\,000$.

As with all images, once the problems become particularly complex we should stop relying on them. Let's take a closing-down sale during which prices are reduced by 20%, then a further 10%, then a final 25%. What was the original price of a scarf now costing £6.75? We could draw three successive bar models, but there is no need once students are confident with decimal multipliers.

Using the fact that percentages have decimal (and fractional) equivalents, we can calculate a reduction of 20%, which results in 80% of the original value, by multiplying by 0.8. Similar multipliers of 0.9 and 0.75 represent the further two reductions, so we have:

$$\text{original price} \times 0.8 \times 0.9 \times 0.75 = £6.75$$
$$\text{original price} = £6.75 \div 0.8 \div 0.9 \div 0.75$$
$$= £12.50$$

We could also have combined the three multipliers to give one single multiplier of $0.8 \times 0.9 \times 0.75 = 0.54$ and divided by this to give the same answer.

Students find it notoriously difficult to work out whether to multiply or divide by a decimal multiplier, which ultimately comes down to a lack of understanding of the situation they are presented with, combined with insecurity over the principle that percentages between 0% and 100% are reductions and those over 100% are increases. Writing out an **equation** using 'original price' and 'new price' (or something similar) often helps to identify the necessary calculations. Taking something like:

original price $\times$ (decimal multiplier for increase or decrease) = new price

and substituting values into the correct places provides a framework for all types of percentage calculations.

 3.1b Preparing to teach – do the mathematics!

Try these questions yourself before proceeding

1 A quick calculation will confirm that 10% of 40 is the same as 40% of 10. Show that a% of b is always the same as b% of a.

2 When a number is cubed the answer is a reduction by 36% of the original number. What could the number be?

3 If m is 25% of n, n is 80% of p, and p is 25% of q, express q as a percentage of m.

The combining of percentages seen in the previous example is called compounding and it is most often taught in the context of compound interest. If a bank applies interest to an account at a rate of 0.4% per month, then the value of the balance, each month, will be 100.4% of the previous balance, or 1.004 times greater. If this interest is applied over six months, then the original balance has been multiplied by 1.004 six times, or by 1.004^6. Hence the compound interest **formula** (which applies to any compounded increase or decrease) is:

original value $\times$ (decimal multiplier for increase or decrease)^n = new value

where n is the number of times this increase or decrease has been applied. This formula bears a striking resemblance to the calculations we did in Section 1.3 to find the value of the **exponential constant**, e. In fact, exponential growth (or decay) is exactly what we are considering here: our decimal multiplier is the **base** of the exponential and n is the **exponent**.

This is the mathematics behind the half-lives of atomic elements in physics or the modelling of population growth in biology. We will return to different types of growth, including exponential growth, in Section 4.2, which brings together numerical principles, sequences and graphs in one of those moments where you see how so much in mathematics is inextricably woven together.

Further exploration

Around 300 BCE, Euclid wrote a treatise called *Elements*, one of the most important mathematical works the world has ever seen. Descartes, of coordinate fame, spent a lot of time on Euclid's geometric ideas, which he used to construct a geometric representation of multiplication that involved scaling lines and making triangles. Take a look into Descartes' work on Euclid's Book VI Proposition 12 to see how a multiplicative product can be constructed from straight lines.

3.2 Ratio

 Try this first

 How is ratio related to proportional thinking?

 If two ratios are equivalent, what equation could be written to link all the numbers in the two ratios?

Ratio work often begins with comparing two quantities in direct proportion, such as the number of black and white beads in the necklace in Figure 3.14, where for every two white beads there are three black, so the ratio of white to black is $2:3$.

Figure 3.14

To consider ratio in more depth, let's return to our scaling diagram from Section 3.1.

We have in Figure 3.15 a picture of the equivalence of $1:4$ and $3:12$, as well as $1:3$ and $4:12$; from this equivalence we get the equations $\frac{12}{4} = \frac{3}{1}$ and $\frac{4}{1} = \frac{12}{3}$. More generally, if $a:b$ is equivalent to $c:d$, then $\frac{d}{c} = \frac{b}{a}$ and $\frac{d}{b} = \frac{c}{a}$. It is, of course, important that students don't confuse this with the fraction of the whole each part takes up, such as the white beads in the necklace occupying $\frac{2}{5}$ of the necklace. It is very common for students to opt for $\frac{2}{3}$ in this case.

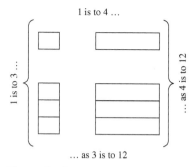

Figure 3.15

Ratio is another topic in which the bar model proves especially effective. Something relatively simple, like splitting £350 in the ratio 4:3, is visualised as in Figure 3.16.

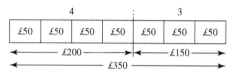

Figure 3.16

More complex problems can also be visualised in this way. Imagine that some money is shared between person A and person B in the ratio 5:3. Person A gives person B £25 and now the money is shared in the ratio 9:7. A bar model, as in Figure 3.17, helps us to work out the amount of money that has been shared.

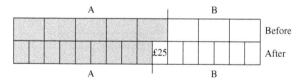

Figure 3.17

If one part of the 16 total parts is worth £25, then the total is £400, originally split in the ratio £250:£150. The image highlights the link between the ratios 5:3, 10:6 and 9:7, and shows clearly that £25 per part when the total is split into 16 parts gives £50 per part when it is split into 8 parts. This is the idea behind inverse proportion (which we will discuss in more detail in Section 3.3): as the number of parts halves, the value of each part doubles.

The point of a bar model is to help students understand the relationship between parts, equivalent parts and the whole in a ratio. Even when they become quite competent it can provide a way into a problem which, without the visual aid, can become quite complex to solve. Our solution in this example involved scaling – turning $5:3$ into $10:6$ to allow us to compare it easily with $9:7$, which has the same number of parts in total. The problem could equally have been solved algebraically, taking the starting amount as x. Originally person A has $\dfrac{5}{8}x$ and person B has $\dfrac{3}{8}x$. When A gives B £25, A has $\dfrac{9}{16}x$, so we have the equation:

$$\frac{5}{8}x - 25 = \frac{9}{16}x$$

$$\frac{1}{16}x = 25$$

$$x = 25 \times 16 = 400$$

The solution requires a good understanding of forming and solving equations, which means students will struggle to access it until they have this underlying knowledge. Most ratio questions in school can be solved without algebra if students practise scaling and finding comparable ratios, but once forming and solving equations are secure this can be a more direct route.

 ## 3.2 Preparing to teach – do the mathematics!

Try this question yourself before proceeding

A group of students is split into those who understand binary, and those who don't (old joke, I know!) in the ratio $1:10$. Those who don't are split in the ratio $4:9$ into those who are bothered by their lack of knowledge and those who aren't.

What percentage of the students are not bothered that they don't understand binary and what is the smallest possible size of this group of students?

 ## Thinking about the classroom

One way to introduce ratio is with counters in two colours, say red and blue. Grouping two reds and three blues shows the ratio $2:3$, but by successively adding in three blues for every two reds we see how $4:6$, $6:9$, $8:12$, ... are equivalent ratios. If 30 counters are to be split in the ratio $2:3$ red to blue, students can move them into groupings two and three at a time until they have used 30 counters.

Once the ideas of ratio and sharing into a ratio are secure, we can start to write down our calculations and introduce images such as the bar model, which phase out the need for counters. We then systematically work towards fluency with ratio without the need for manipulatives or a picture.

Working with ratio is a very important skill; it is often the link between proportionality and other areas of mathematics. For instance, enlargements of shapes, similarity (with length, area and volume) and trigonometry all rely on ratio.

The most famous ratio?

Here we are going to delve into an interesting area of mathematics that isn't on the school curriculum but which links together many of the strands we have already looked at.

One of the problems dealt with in classical Greek mathematics was that of the search for the most 'pleasing' way to divide a line. The Greeks considered that if a line was divided into two parts such that the ratio of the longer to the shorter part was the same as the ratio of the whole line to the longer part, then this would be the perfect division, or *golden section*. Let's take a look at this idea. An example of such a line is shown in Figure 3.18.

Figure 3.18

By naming the longer section a and the shorter b we have the ratio $a : b$ equivalent to $a + b : a$.

$$\frac{a+b}{a} = \frac{a}{b}$$

$$\frac{a}{a} + \frac{b}{a} = \frac{a}{b}$$

$$1 + \frac{b}{a} = \frac{a}{b}$$

This is useful because $\frac{a}{b}$ is the reciprocal of $\frac{b}{a}$, so we will let $x = \frac{a}{b}$ and $\frac{1}{x} = \frac{b}{a}$. This transforms the equation into:

$$1 + \frac{1}{x} = x$$

$$x + 1 = x^2$$

$$x^2 - x - 1 = 0$$

Solving this **quadratic** equation gives $x = \frac{1 \pm \sqrt{5}}{2}$.

One of these two solutions is negative and doesn't make sense as the ratio of one length to another, although we will return to it shortly. This means $\frac{a}{b} = \frac{1 + \sqrt{5}}{2}$ and the line must be divided in the ratio $\frac{1 + \sqrt{5}}{2} : 1$. This rather interesting irrational, algebraic number (see Section 2.3) is approximately equal to $1.618\,033\,9887$ and is called the *golden ratio*. We give it the Greek letter phi, φ, and find that it is one of those fascinating irrational numbers, like π and e, that comes up in different places and has some lovely properties.

For a start, look at the other solution to that quadratic equation, $\dfrac{1-\sqrt{5}}{2}$. This is approximately $-0.618\,033\,9887...$, which bears a good similarity to φ. The interesting quality of these **roots** is that their **sum** is 1 and their product is -1, meaning one is the negative reciprocal of the other. This makes sense in the context of Section 2.3, where we saw that the roots of a quadratic equation sum to $\dfrac{-b}{a}$ and multiply to give $\dfrac{c}{a}$. Considering the quadratic here uses $a=1$, $b=-1$ and $c=-1$. This means that φ has the unique property that its reciprocal is one less than itself, or $\varphi-1=\dfrac{1}{\varphi}$.

As a number fact this is interesting, but not enough on its own to make φ a notable number (there had to be a number for which that fact is true, just as there is a number whose reciprocal is equal to 2 less than itself, or 3 less, and so on). What else makes φ so worthy of note?

Its **continued fraction** representation is lovely, for a start. We saw in Section 2.3 that the quadratic irrationals have periodic continued fractions, so what does φ look like in this form?[2]

$$\varphi \approx 1.618 = 1+\cfrac{1}{1+\cfrac{1}{1+\cfrac{1}{1+\cfrac{1}{1+\cfrac{1}{1+...}}}}}$$

This has to be the simplest of all continued fractions, but the numerical loveliness doesn't stop there. There are also such things as continued square roots, which were studied in some depth by the early twentieth century Indian mathematician Srinivasa Ramanujan. Going back to the original equation that generated φ, $x^2-x-1=0$, rearranging to $x^2=1+x$ and writing the actual solution, φ, in place of x gives us:

$$\varphi^2 = 1+\varphi$$
$$\varphi = \sqrt{1+\varphi}$$

---

[2] To learn how to find a continued fraction of a quadratic irrational number, see the quiz at the end of Chapter 3. The process for a rational number is in Section 1.3.

The clever step comes now. By replacing the φ inside the **surd** with what φ is equal to, $\sqrt{1+\varphi}$, and continuing this ad infinitum, we get:

$$\varphi = \sqrt{1+\sqrt{1+\sqrt{1+\sqrt{1+\ldots}}}}$$

This process can be done for any quadratic equation, but it is only *this* quadratic equation that gives this most straightforward of continued square roots.

Elegant as these two representations are, they are merely a result of the simple **coefficients** in the quadratic equation, so they do not lend the number any specialness other than it happening to be the root of this quadratic. As such, the golden ratio is not remotely as important to mathematics as π, e or i. It does, however, arise in other interesting circumstances. We can generate a golden rectangle, which is a rectangle that you want to divide into two pieces such that one is a square and the other is a rectangle, but where this smaller rectangle is in the same proportions as the original rectangle. It would look something like the rectangle in Figure 3.19, and the division is such that $a : (a+b)$ is equivalent to $b : a$, giving us the equation:

$$\frac{a+b}{a} = \frac{a}{b}$$

which is, of course, exactly the equation that gave rise to φ earlier. If you iterate the process, dividing each rectangle into a square and a rectangle such that every smaller rectangle is similar to those before, you create the image in Figure 3.20, over which can be drawn the *golden spiral*.

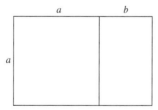

Figure 3.19

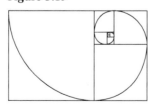

Figure 3.20

The golden ratio can also be found in certain number sequences and, as a consequence, even in Pascal's triangle (Section 2.1), and we will return to this in Section 4.1. It appears in many geometric constructions, such as in a regular pentagon, where the length of a diagonal and a side are in the golden ratio.

There are claims that the golden ratio has been used historically in art and architecture; although many such claims seem difficult to substantiate there is a small number of modern architects and artists who have attested to its deliberate use.

3.3 Direct and inverse proportion

 Try this first

If one quantity doubles, what happens to another quantity that is related to the first by:

a. direct proportion

b. direct square proportion

c. inverse proportion

d. inverse square proportion?

We have already looked briefly at what it means for two quantities to be in direct or inverse proportion (in Sections 3.1 and 3.2). In this section, we address this more formally and abstractly.

If two quantities are linked by a constant – such that one is always double the other, or five-twelfths of the other, say – then those quantities are in direct proportion. Clearly if one quantity is 0, so is the other. Therefore, we can represent these quantities, call them y and x, and all their possible pairs of values, on a graph with equation $y = kx$, where k is the **constant** of proportionality, as in Figure 3.21.

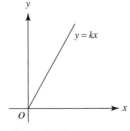

Figure 3.21

Note that k is the **gradient** of the graph, which means it can be interpreted as 'for every 1 unit that x increases, y increases by k units'.

If such a relationship exists between y and x, we can write that $y \propto x$, read 'y is (directly) proportional to x'. The origin of the proportionality symbol, ∞, is particularly uninteresting. It first appears in the 1748 book by William Emerson, *The Doctrine of Fluxions*[3], which says 'To the common Algebraic Characters already receiv'd I add this ∞, which signifies a general Proportion.' There is no indication of why the symbol was chosen, so in this case we'll have to allow Emerson his whimsy (and remember not to confuse it with the Greek letter alpha, α).

There are plenty of instances of direct proportion that we can use as examples to our students:

- If a car is travelling at a constant speed, distance ∞ time and speed is the constant of proportionality; if you double the distance you travel, you will double the time it takes to get there.

- The force applied to a spring ∞ the extension in the spring (Hooke's law).

- The volume of a gas ∞ the temperature of the gas (Charles' law).

If we know one pair of values in this proportional relationship, we can use it to find the constant of proportionality and then any other pairs of values.

For instance, a force of $10\,\text{N}$ extends a spring by $12\,\text{cm}$. What force will extend the string by $15\,\text{cm}$? If force is directly proportional to extension, $F \propto e$, then $F = ke$ and we can substitute the given values of F and e into the equation to find k (using $12\,\text{cm} = 0.12\,\text{m}$).

$$10 = 0.12k$$
$$k = \frac{10}{0.12} = \frac{250}{3}$$
$$F = \frac{250}{3}e$$

The formula we arrived at for F in terms of e holds true for any other values of F and e in this example. So when $e = 0.15$, $F = \frac{250}{3} \times 0.15 = 12.5\,\text{N}$.

 3.3 Preparing to teach – do the mathematics!

Try this question yourself before proceeding

The gradient of a straight line is directly proportional to its y-intercept. Where does the line cross the x-axis?

---

[3] Emerson was a mechanics specialist following in the steps of Sir Isaac Newton (who used the term *fluxion* for what we now know as a *derivative* in calculus).

Proportion does not have to be linear, however. The kinetic energy of an object $\propto$ the *square* of its velocity, as seen in the formula $KE = \frac{1}{2}mv^2$, where m is the mass of the object. In this example, the constant of proportionality is $\frac{1}{2}m$ and a graph of the relationship would look something like that shown in Figure 3.22.

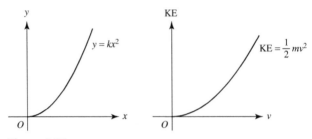

Figure 3.22

Inverse proportion relates two **variables** such that when one increases by a certain proportion, the other decreases – for instance, when one doubles, the other halves. In an electrical circuit, the resistance of a wire is inversely proportional to the cross-sectional area of the wire, so as the wire gets thicker, the resistance decreases. Inverse proportion is written $y \propto \frac{1}{x}$, or $y = \frac{k}{x}$, since $k \times \frac{1}{x} \equiv \frac{k}{x}$.

One of the most famous laws of proportionality throughout science is the *inverse-square law*. This is when $y \propto \frac{1}{x^2}$, or $y = \frac{k}{x^2}$. The intensity of light is subject to the inverse-square law in that it is inversely proportional to the square of the distance from the light source. Looking at the picture in Figure 3.23, person B is three times as far from the light source as person A, so they will receive $\frac{1}{3^2} = \frac{1}{9}$ the intensity of the light.

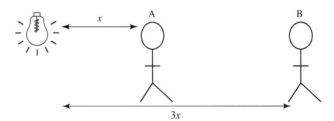

Figure 3.23

Figure 3.24 shows the proportional relationships $y \propto \dfrac{1}{x}$ and $y \propto \dfrac{1}{x^2}$.

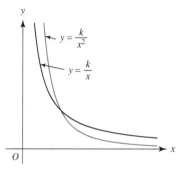

Figure 3.24

They are not the complete graphs of $y = \dfrac{k}{x}$ or $y = \dfrac{k}{x^2}$, but instead show the first quadrant, since they represent physical quantities that take positive values.

 Discuss

What examples of different types of proportion do you know or can you find from other fields (especially science and technology)?

 Thinking about the classroom

Solving questions of proportionality involves a number of steps that can be overwhelming for students, so breaking down the process is very important. Each proportionality question tends to follow a similar process.

1 Write a statement of proportionality using $\propto$.

2 Write a formula from this using k.

3 Use a pair of numbers given to determine k.

4 Write the formula again with the numerical value of k.

5 Use the formula to find missing values.

Of course, the implementation of the steps will look very different depending on the type of proportionality involved, and there are plenty of places for students to trip up – from interpreting the type of proportionality in question to incorrectly rearranging equations. As with most things, never rush through the process and allow plenty of time to practise component parts of a process.

3.4 Scientific forms

 Try this first

The prefix 'centi-' means 'hundredth', so a 'centimetre' is one hundredth of a metre. Which other SI prefixes do you know and what do they mean?

Standard form

Mathematics has a very clever way of dealing with very large and very small numbers, and it's intrinsically linked to place value and powers of ten. Firstly, remind yourself of the function of positive and negative **indices**.

$$10^3 = 1000$$
$$10^2 = 100$$
$$10^1 = 10$$
$$10^0 = 1$$
$$10^{-1} = \frac{1}{10} = 0.1$$
$$10^{-2} = \frac{1}{100} = 0.01$$
$$10^{-3} = \frac{1}{1000} = 0.001$$

We can take any number and write it as a **multiple** of any power of 10. For instance, the number 299 792 458, if measuring in ms^{-1}, is the speed of light in a vacuum. For sake of ease, let's round this number to 300 000 000 ms^{-1}. This could be written in all these ways and more:

$$3000 \times 10^5$$
$$30 \times 10^7$$
$$3 \times 10^8$$
$$0.03 \times 10^{10}$$
$$3\,000\,000\,000 \times 10^{-1}$$

The third of these ways is called standard form, which is where a number is expressed in the form $a \times 10^b$, where $1 \le a < 10$ and $b \in \mathbb{Z}$ (read 'b is in the integers'; we encountered this notation in Section 1.3).

In some countries this form is called scientific form, by virtue of its ubiquity in science. It is extremely useful for working with numbers that could otherwise be hard to read or think about clearly. Take the width of an atom, which is around 0.000 000 000 5 m. In standard form this would be written as 5×10^{-10} m, since the digit 5 has to move 10 places to get to the units position. This number in standard form is much easier to read and compare with other small numbers.

Multiplication and division are quite straightforward when in standard form. We utilise commutativity and **index** laws to perform these calculations and very often have to adjust our answer to put it into standard form. Numbers in standard form tend to be presented in brackets, which can cause some confusion as these brackets are sometimes completely unnecessary[4].

$$(6.1 \times 10^{-5}) \times (4 \times 10^{3}) = 6.1 \times 10^{-5} \times 4 \times 10^{3}$$
$$= 6.1 \times 4 \times 10^{-5} \times 10^{3}$$
$$= 24.4 \times 10^{-2}$$
$$= 2.44 \times 10^{-1}$$

You can see that we added the indices, since their base was the same, and in the last step we divided 24.4 by 10 (to ensure that $1 \leq a < 10$). This meant we had to multiply our power of 10 by 10 to 'balance' out, resulting in the power of 10 increasing by 1.

Division follows the same process, but note that the brackets here *are* necessary to ensure the correct order of operations is followed. A division with numbers in standard form is probably clearer when presented as a fraction:

$$(2 \times 10^{12}) \div (3 \times 10^{-9}) = \frac{2 \times 10^{12}}{3 \times 10^{-9}}$$
$$= (2 \div 3) \times (10^{12} \div 10^{-9})$$
$$= 0.\dot{6} \times 10^{21}$$
$$= 6.\dot{6} \times 10^{20}$$

Again, in the last step we had to turn the number into standard form. This time we multiplied $0.\dot{6}$ by 10 so we had to reduce our index by 1, which is equivalent to dividing by 10. What could go wrong if we didn't put brackets around the two standard form numbers at the start of the calculation?

Addition and subtraction with numbers in standard form require some fluency in manipulating the form so that we can apply **distributivity**. Take $(5.3 \times 10^{8}) + (9 \times 10^{11})$. We can do this without having to turn the numbers into their ordinary form by manipulating one to have the same power of 10 as the other.

---

[4] Never be surprised by the mess that brackets cause. You can simply remove the brackets around the numbers in standard form here, but why can't you do the same when multiplying two bracketed **binomials** in algebra? It may seem obvious to you, but it will not always be clear to students.

$$(5.3 \times 10^8) + (9 \times 10^{11}) = (5.3 \times 10^8) + (9000 \times 10^8)$$ Write the second number as a multiple of 10^8

$$= (9000 + 5.3) \times 10^8$$ Apply distributivity (you're **factorising** here)

$$= 9005.3 \times 10^8$$ Simplify

$$= 9.0053 \times 10^{11}$$ Convert to standard form

How would the process have looked different if we had written the first number as a multiple of 10^{11} instead?

Engineering form

Engineering form is a variation of the scientific form that enables us to use the standard SI prefixes with ease. Here are some of the most common prefixes.

tera, T	giga, G	mega, M	kilo, k	milli, m	micro, μ	nano, n	pico, p
$\times 10^{12}$	$\times 10^9$	$\times 10^6$	$\times 10^3$	$\times 10^{-3}$	$\times 10^{-6}$	$\times 10^{-9}$	$\times 10^{-12}$

This means that our atom from earlier, having a width of 5×10^{-10} m, can be expressed in terms of standard prefixes with some manipulation. It is 0.5×10^{-9} m, which is 0.5 nm, or 500×10^{-12} m, which is 500 pm. Many calculators have a button for engineering form, often labelled ENG; this will take a number through consecutive powers of 10 that are multiples of three (in both directions).

 3.4 Preparing to teach – do the mathematics!

Try these questions yourself before proceeding

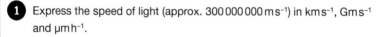 Express the speed of light (approx. $300\,000\,000$ m s^{-1}) in km s^{-1}, Gm s^{-1} and μm h^{-1}.

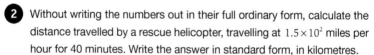 Without writing the numbers out in their full ordinary form, calculate the distance travelled by a rescue helicopter, travelling at 1.5×10^2 miles per hour for 40 minutes. Write the answer in standard form, in kilometres.

Quiz 3

1. The population of bacteria in a dish doubles every day. After 8 days there are 28 million bacteria. After how many days are there 7 million bacteria?

2. Which values of $n \in \mathbb{N}$ would make $(-1)^n$ positive and which values would make it negative?

3. Write the number 6 in standard form.

4. Two numbers are in the ratio $2:1$. When 3 is subtracted from both numbers, the new numbers are in the ratio $9:4$. What were the original two numbers?

5. A milliner sells three types of hat: boaters, berets and fedoras. One day when she opens her shop, the ratio of boaters to berets is $5:4$ and the ratio of berets to fedoras is $3:2$. The milliner has more than 50 hats (in total) in stock. What is the smallest possible number of each type of hat in the shop?

6. Evaluate the following, without a calculator, leaving your answer in standard form.
$$\frac{\left(1 \times 10^{-6}\right) + \left(2 \times 10^{-5}\right)}{\left(430 \times 10^{4}\right) - \left(2.2 \times 10^{6}\right)}$$

The next two questions move well beyond the school curriculum but require only school-level mathematics to complete.

7. We saw φ as a continued fraction in Section 3.2, a representation derived from the quadratic equation that gave rise to φ. We can do this for any quadratic irrational number. Since $\sqrt{2}$ is between 1 and 2 we could write it as $1 + x$, where x is its decimal part. This gives us the equation $\sqrt{2} = 1 + x$ and squaring both sides gives us:
$$2 = (1 + x)^2 = 1 + 2x + x^2$$

We can rearrange this to give $1 = x^2 + 2x$ and then divide the whole equation by x to get $\dfrac{1}{x} = 2 + x$. If we reciprocate both sides we have $x = \dfrac{1}{2 + x}$, which will generate a continued fraction by successively replacing x with $\dfrac{1}{2 + x}$. This gives:

$$x = \cfrac{1}{2 + \cfrac{1}{2 + \cfrac{1}{2 + \cfrac{1}{2 + \ldots}}}}$$

Since $\sqrt{2} = 1 + x$, we now know that $\sqrt{2} = 1 + \cfrac{1}{2 + \cfrac{1}{2 + \cfrac{1}{2 + \cfrac{1}{2 + \ldots}}}}$

Using this process, find the continued fraction representation of $\sqrt{5}$.

8. φ is the number whose reciprocal is one less than itself. Thinking about how we can write this algebraically, what is the value of the number whose reciprocal is n less than itself? Express this number as a continued fraction and as a continued square root.

Answers to each Quiz, Try this first *and* Preparing to teach *are at the back of the book.*

Chapter 4

Algebra II: Patterns and proving

4.1 Patterns and sequences

> ✔ **Try this first**
>
> **1** What type of sequence are the following all examples of?
>
>   a. 5, 10, 20, 40, …
>
>   b. 4, 5, 9, 14, 23, …
>
>   c. −8, −11, −14, −17, …
>
>   d. 0, 1, 5, 12, 22, …
>
> **2** What is the difference between a position-to-**term** rule and a term-to-term rule?

Carl Friedrich Gauss was born in 1777 in Brunswick, Germany. When he was 8 years old his teacher, eager to keep the little prodigy busy, asked him to **sum** all the **integers** from 1 to 100. Only a minute later, Gauss gave the answer of 5050, no doubt shocking his teacher, and so began one of the most influential mathematical careers of the past 250 years.

The tale (the veracity of which is questionable) goes on to explain that Gauss spotted that you can pair up the integers, starting from the outside and working in, into 50 pairs (as shown in Figure 4.1). The sum of each pair is 101, and the sum of the whole is therefore 5050.

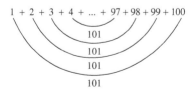

Figure 4.1

Gauss went on to complete his greatest mathematical work at the age of 21 and had a huge influence not only on mathematics but also on physics, working in optics, geophysics, electrics and astronomy. What Gauss understood and exploited was that mathematics is underpinned by patterns, and by looking for the patterns we can make sense of complex problems and generalise them. Once we know how to sum up the integers from 1 to 100, we know how to sum up any series of consecutive integers from 1 to n, using the same process.

Linearity: arithmetic sequences

There are all sorts of interesting patterns and number sequences that we study in school mathematics but, as is the case with novice students, their connections to other areas of study often go unnoticed. Take linear sequences, for instance, sometimes called arithmetic sequences – those where the terms in the sequence increase or decrease by the same number, called the common difference. The multiplication tables are the most basic examples of these: the five times table, for instance, has common difference 5, first term 5, second term 10, eighth term 40 and nth term $5n$. We use the letter n to denote the position of a term in the sequence, so the general position-to-term rule is called the nth term.

The table below shows the same for the six times table.

Position	1	2	3	4	...	50	n
Term	6	12	18	24	...	300	$6n$

And below for a different sequence, related to the six times table, which increases by 6 each time but whose terms are all 3 less than the six times table.

Position	1	2	3	4	...	50	n
6 times table	6	12	18	24	...	300	$6n$
Sequence	3	9	15	21	...	297	$6n - 3$

A linear sequence, and its relationship to the multiplication tables, can be seen very clearly on a number line or grid, as in Figure 4.2. Both of these illustrate how, in the case of the sequence $6n - 3$, the sequence is just a shift in the six times table.

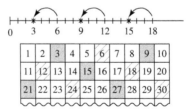

Figure 4.2

Students benefit hugely from seeing the link between the multiplication tables and linear sequences, and emphasising this helps to reduce common errors like writing $n + 6$ for a sequence whose common difference is 6. Without even knowing it, students are confusing the nth term of a sequence with a term-to-term rule, or recurrence relation.

A recurrence relation is a way of describing a sequence recursively, that is, in terms of itself. We use u_n to represent a term in a sequence, so the first term is u_1, the second u_2, the nth u_n. We must state the first term before describing how each term is generated from preceding ones in the recurrence relation. For the sequence $6n - 3$, which starts at 3 and has common difference 6, the recurrence relation would be given by:

$$u_1 = 3$$
$$u_{n+1} = u_n + 6$$

which represents 'start at 3, find a term by adding 6 to the preceding term'.

These sequences and their nth terms are something we've encountered already in a slightly different guise. Notice that the table is identical to a table of integer values produced by the **equation** of the line $y = 6x - 3$ and would, when graphed, lie on a straight line of **gradient** 6 and y-intercept -3. Finding the nth term, or position-to-term rule, of a sequence is exactly the same thing as identifying the equation of a straight line on which those pairs of values lie. Indeed, all arithmetic sequences can be viewed through the lens of linear graphs. Figure 4.3 plots the points generated by $y = 6x$ and $y = 6x - 3$.

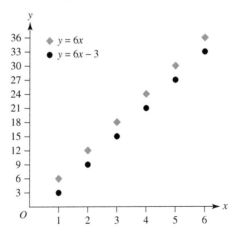

Figure 4.3

If we plot the pairs (position, term) on the Cartesian grid, we see two linear graphs of the same gradient, but our new sequence has translated the first graph down by 3 (more on this in Section 4.2).

All these principles hold when a sequence decreases. Take the sequence 2, -2, -6, -10, ... This goes down in fours, so it is related to the -4

times table (if such a thing exists!) and lies on a translation of the graph $y = -4x$.

Position	1	2	3	4	...	50	n
−4 times table	−4	−8	−12	−16	...	−200	$-4n$
Term	2	−2	−6	−10	...	−194	$-4n + 6$ or $6 - 4n$

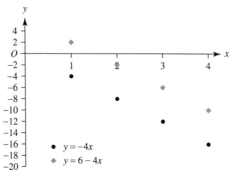

Figure 4.4

A visual model of a sequence reinforces the interpretation of the gradient and y-intercept of a line. Take the simple image of patterns shown in Figure 4.5.

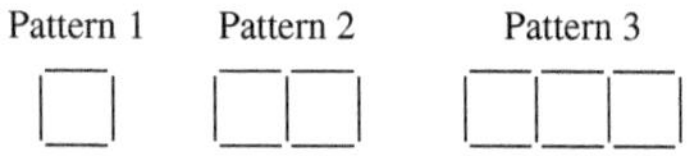

Figure 4.5

A sequence can be made from the number of sticks in each pattern. The first term is 4 and three more sticks are added each time, which produces the sequence 4, 7, 10, 13, ... The nth term **formula** can be seen if we isolate the first vertical stick in each pattern. Pattern 1 has one set of three sticks, pattern 2 has two sets of three sticks, pattern 3 has three sets, and so on, but each pattern has one isolated stick on the left, showing us the nth term is $3n + 1$. This could transfer to a graph, as shown in Figure 4.6, which starts at 1 (the y-intercept) and has a gradient of 3, giving the first term of 4.

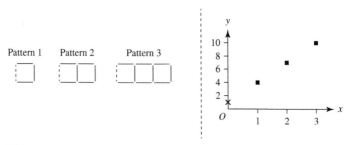

Figure 4.6

4.1a Preparing to teach – do the mathematics!

Try these questions yourself before proceeding

1 Find the nth term of the sequence 3, −5, 7, −9, 11, −13, ...

2 Explain the nth term of the sequence illustrated in Figure 4.7, using only the pictures.

Pattern 1   Pattern 2   Pattern 3

Figure 4.7

Before we move on, it is worth considering why linear sequences are also called arithmetic sequences. You may or may not have noticed that if you take any three consecutive terms in any linear sequence, then the mean (or, more precisely, the arithmetic mean) of the first and third of these terms is equal to the second. Take the sequence 13, 17, 21, 25, ..., and you see that $\frac{13+21}{2} = 17$ and $\frac{17+25}{2} = 21$. More generally, if a linear sequence has nth term $an+b$, $(n+1)$th term $a(n+1)+b$ and $(n+2)$th term $a(n+2)+b$, then the arithmetic mean of the first and third of these terms is:

$$\frac{(an+b)+(a(n+2)+b)}{2} = \frac{an+b+an+2a+b}{2}$$
$$= \frac{2an+2a+2b}{2}$$
$$= an+a+b$$
$$= a(n+1)+b$$

which is the middle term of the three.

It is the link to the arithmetic mean that gives arithmetic sequences their name. The arithmetic mean is so named because the ancient Greeks generally used arithmetic to deal with problems involving addition and subtraction. In contrast, they generally used geometry to deal with problems involving multiplication and division, which leads us onto our next type of sequence.

 Thinking about the classroom

Encourage familiarity with numerical, algebraic *and* pictorial representations of sequences. Pictorial representations help students to think in terms of what remains constant and what changes, which reinforces the meaning of the nth term formula.

Non-linearity: geometric sequences

A geometric sequence is one where, instead of adding a **constant** to get from one term to the next, we multiply by a constant, called the common ratio. A recurrence relation for a geometric sequence would be of the form

$$u_1 = a$$
$$u_{n+1} = ru_n$$

where r is the common ratio. An example of this might be the sequence where $u_1 = 3$ and $u_{n+1} = 2u_n$, meaning you start at 3 and multiply by 2 each time, generating the sequence 3, 6, 12, 24, 48, ...

To consider the nth term of this geometric sequence let's look at each term as presented in this table.

Position	1	2	3	4	...	10	n
Generation of term	3	3×2	$3 \times 2 \times 2 = 3 \times 2^2$	$3 \times 2 \times 2 \times 2 = 3 \times 2^3$	...	3×2^9	$3 \times 2^{n-1}$
Term	3	6	12	24	...	1536	$3 \times 2^{n-1}$

Notice that the number of times you multiply by 2 is always one less than the position of the term, hence 2^{n-1} in the nth term. The **expression** $3 \times 2^{n-1}$ looks very similar to the formula for compound interest we saw in Section 3.1 – just another time when two different mathematical topics are, in essence, the same thing. Compound interest is an application of a geometric sequence, whose general nth term is of the form ar^{n-1}, where the first term is a and the common ratio is r.

Geometric sequences owe their name to the fact that if you take any three consecutive terms, then the geometric mean of the first and third of these terms is equal to the second. The geometric mean is not something we tend to encounter in school mathematics but it is one of three important means, the other two being the arithmetic mean and the harmonic mean. The geometric mean of two numbers a and b is given by $\sqrt{ab}$ and owes its title to the ancient Greeks' use of geometry to approach problems of multiplication. It is the solution to the geometric problem 'What is the length of the side of a square with the same area as a rectangle with side lengths a and b?'; it has applications in physics and finance, and is useful when a mathematical model involves **exponential** growth or decay.

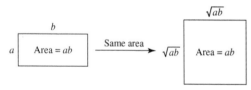

Figure 4.8

Further exploration

Arithmetic and geometric sequences are studied in some depth in advanced mathematics. When the terms in a sequence are summed up this is called a series.

We referred to the common ratio between terms as r. When $r > 1$ or $r < -1$ the terms in geometric sequences grow indefinitely larger, but when $-1 < r < 1$ subsequent terms get smaller and smaller. When all the terms in such a sequence are summed up, there is a limit – a number the sum approaches but will never go past. This idea underpins Zeno's Paradoxes, including the famous one about the race between Achilles and the tortoise, which prompt us to think about the confusing and counter-intuitive nature of infinity.

Non-linearity: quadratic sequences

Consider the sequence of square numbers 1, 4, 9, 16, ..., whose nth term would be simply n^2. Since the nth term has **degree** 2 we call this sequence a **quadratic** sequence. More generally, a quadratic sequence is one that can be generated from a position-to-term rule of the form $an^2 + bn + c$, which we know is the general form of a quadratic, looked at in Section 2.3.

These sequences have some very interesting behaviours. Take the sequence generated by $n^2 + 4n + 1$, seen in the following table and plotted on axes in Figure 4.9.

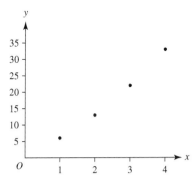

Figure 4.9

Position	1	2	3	4
Term	6	13	22	33

It will come as no surprise that the sequence lies on the graph of $y = x^2 + 4x + 1$, but it is in pictorial form that the patterns are particularly lovely.

We will represent the sequence n^2 using, obviously, squares, as in Figure 4.10.

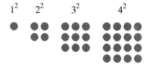

Figure 4.10

The sequence $n^2 + 4n + 1$ adds the linear sequence $4n + 1$ to n^2, and we could picture it, using the areas of squares and rectangles, as shown in Figure 4.11.

Figure 4.11

From the shading in Figure 4.11 we can see how the nth term formula arises, but we can reach this formula another way. A general term in the sequence is represented as in Figure 4.12.

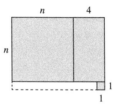

Figure 4.12

We can find an expression for the area of the whole rectangle (indicated by the dotted lines) and then subtract the area of the white space. In this case, the large rectangle has area $(n + 1)(n + 4)$ and the white space is $(n + 3) \times 1$. This gives the shaded area as:

$$(n + 1)(n + 4) - (n + 3) \equiv \left(n^2 + 5n + 4\right) - (n + 3) \equiv n^2 + 4n + 1$$

To create a recurrence relation for a quadratic sequence such as this, we need to look at what happens from term to term. Our sequence goes 6, 13, 22, 33, ...; the difference between the first and second terms is 7, between the second and third is 9, between the third and fourth is 11. It becomes apparent that the differences themselves are following the linear sequence 7, 9, 11, ..., whose nth term is $2n + 5$.

From this, we see that to get from one term to the next we have to add on successive terms in the sequence $2n + 5$ and the recurrence relation must be:

$$u_1 = 6$$
$$u_{n+1} = u_n + 2n + 5$$

In general, the recurrence relation for a quadratic sequence will be of the form $u_{n+1} = u_n + an + b$, indicating that the differences between terms form a linear sequence.

Finding the nth term of a quadratic sequence is a little more involved. Let's delve into it algebraically from the start. If $u_n = an^2 + bn + c$, then we have the following terms.

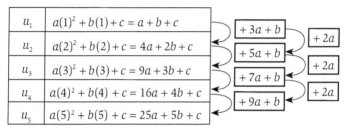

The difference between the second and first terms is $3a + b$, that between the third and second is $5a + b$. The difference between these differences, called the *second difference*, is $2a$, and we know that this second difference will always be $2a$ since the first differences form a linear sequence. We now know that the second difference in a quadratic sequence is always twice a, the **coefficient** of n^2.

Let's use this to find the nth term of the sequence $-5, -4, 1, 10, 23, \ldots$.

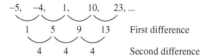

Figure 4.13

The first differences, as shown in Figure 4.13, are 1, 5, 9, 13, ... and the second differences are all 4, which means this sequence begins $2n^2$. To find out what $bn + c$ is, we need to subtract $2n^2$ from each term.

Position	1	2	3	4	5	n
Sequence $= 2n^2 + bn + c$	-5	-4	1	10	23	
$2n^2$	2	8	18	32	50	$2n^2$
Sequence $-2n^2 = bn + c$	-7	-12	-17	-22	-27	$-5n - 2$

The last row of the table shows a linear sequence, with nth term $-5n - 2$. We can see that each term in the sequence is equal to the sum of the two cells below it, telling us that the nth term of the quadratic sequence is $2n^2 - 5n - 2$.

4.1b Preparing to teach – do the mathematics!

Try this question yourself before proceeding

We have seen how the coefficient of n^2 is half the second difference in a quadratic sequence. Using a similar technique, how can we find the coefficient of n^3 in a **cubic** sequence, or of n^4 in a quartic sequence? What is the coefficient of n^p in a sequence of degree p?

There are two very famous quadratic sequences: the square numbers (illustrated in Figure 4.10) and their closely-related cousin the triangular numbers (Figure 4.14).

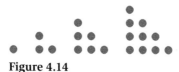

Figure 4.14

We know the square numbers go 1, 4, 9, 16, ... and their nth term is n^2. The triangular numbers are perhaps the simplest of quadratic sequences: start at 1, add 2, then 3, then 4, then 5, and so on. The nth term of these could be found in the way we detailed earlier, but it is much more satisfying to do it pictorially, exploiting their geometry to our advantage. Take the second triangle, representing the second term of 3, rotate a copy of it 180° and this copy will fit with the original to make a 2×3 rectangle. Now take the fourth triangle, representing the fourth term of 10, rotate a copy 180° and it fits to make a 4×5 rectangle.

Figure 4.15

More generally, take the nth triangle, rotate a copy 180° and it fits to make an $n \times (n+1)$ rectangle. Since these rectangles are formed by two copies of the original, the triangle must be half of the rectangle, and we have the nth term of the triangular numbers: $\dfrac{n(n+1)}{2}$ or $\dfrac{1}{2}n(n+1)$.

 4.1c Preparing to teach – do the mathematics!

Try this question yourself before proceeding

Polygonal numbers are sequences of numbers that can be represented by polygons. We have met the triangular and square numbers already. The pentagonal numbers are shown in Figure 4.16, and the hexagonal numbers in Figure 4.17.

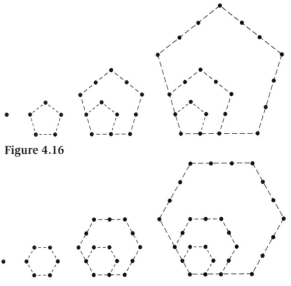

Figure 4.16

Figure 4.17

What are the nth terms of the pentagonal and hexagonal numbers? What about the heptagonal, octagonal, nonagonal, ... numbers? You should notice a pattern in these formulae. Use this to find a formula for the nth term of the p-gonal numbers, where p is the number of sides in the polygon.

Non-linearity: The Fibonacci sequence

Leonardo of Pisa, commonly known as Fibonacci, was a prolific mathematician in the thirteenth century. Fibonacci was the son of an Italian merchant and spent years travelling around the Mediterranean with his father. On his travels he discovered that merchants were using a system of numerals far superior to the Roman numerals to which he was accustomed. The system they were using is now called the Hindu–Arabic numerals and originated in ancient India, later to be recorded and explained by al-Khwarizmi (he of solving equations fame whom we met in Section 2.1) in the ninth century.[1]

Fibonacci published his book *Liber Abaci* (*The Book of Calculation*) in 1202, in which he explained this wonderful new number system, the one we still use today. Also in the book is a curious investigation into the population growth

---

[1] Al-Khwarizmi's name was written in Latin as Algoritmi, and it is from this that we get our word *algorithm* for a set of instructions that can be followed to solve a problem, such as solving an equation. Algorithms came into their own in the twentieth century with the dawn of the computer age but, as with most things in mathematics, can trace their origins back by millennia.

of rabbits, which generates a number sequence that first appeared in Indian mathematics around 700 CE but which we now call the Fibonacci sequence.

Fibonacci's rabbits mate and give birth like clockwork: a newborn male and female are placed together in a field; once they are one month old they mate and a month later they produce another boy–girl pair. The rabbits then reproduce once every month, and every new pair obeys the same rules. These (immortal, by the way) rabbits continue to reproduce and the number of pairs in the field (they aren't adventurous, they stay in the field) follows an interesting sequence. Figure 4.18 represents each pair of rabbits as a labelled circle, showing us how the sequence is formed.

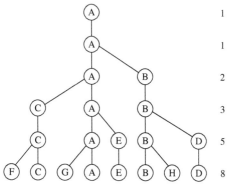

Figure 4.18

The sequence produced goes 1, 1, 2, 3, 5, 8, 13, ..., where each number is the sum of the preceding two. The recurrence relation for the sequence is therefore:

$$u_{n+2} = u_{n+1} + u_n$$
$$u_1 = 1, u_2 = 1$$

Although the terms in this sequence get larger and larger, something very interesting happens if you take a term and divide it by its predecessor, especially if you continue this as the sequence goes on. Consider the following table.

n	1	2	3	4	5	6	7	8	9	10	11	12
u_n	1	1	2	3	5	8	13	21	34	55	89	144
$\dfrac{u_n}{u_{n-1}}$	$\dfrac{1}{1}$ $=1$	$\dfrac{2}{1}$ $=2$	$\dfrac{3}{2}$ $=1.5$	$\dfrac{5}{3}$ $=1.\dot{6}$	$\dfrac{8}{5}$ $=1.6$	$\dfrac{13}{8}$ $=1.625$	$\dfrac{21}{13}$ $=1.615$	$\dfrac{34}{21}$ $=1.619$	$\dfrac{55}{34}$ $=1.618$	$\dfrac{89}{55}$ $=1.618$	$\dfrac{144}{89}$ $=1.618$

These consecutive **quotients** oscillate but start to settle around the number 1.618 (to 4 s.f.), which you will remember from Section 3.2 – the golden ratio. In fact, any Fibonacci-style sequence – where the recurrence relation is followed but which has different values for the first and second terms – has the same property, in that successive quotients converge to φ. In Figure 4.19 you will see this for the standard Fibonacci sequence (A), the one where $u_1 = 2$ and $u_2 = 1$ (B), and the one where $u_1 = 9$ and $u_2 = 32$ (C).[2]

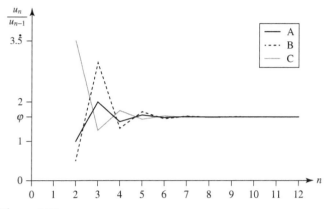

Figure 4.19

Incidentally, in Section 2.1 we met Pascal's triangle, which we said contained patterns other than the coefficients of the **binomial expansion**. It turns out that the Fibonacci sequence (and, by consequence, the golden ratio φ) is hidden in the triangle – but you have to look carefully, as you will see in Figure 4.20.

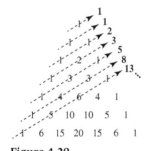

Figure 4.20

 Further exploration

There is a formula for the nth term of the Fibonacci sequence, called Binet's formula, which involves φ. Its derivation and extension to general Fibonacci sequences make an interesting investigation.

Pascal's triangle also contains the square and triangular numbers – can you find them?

---

[2] No reason why *those* numbers, I used a random number generator.

4.2 Functions and graphs

✅ Try this first

1 What is the importance of **function** notation? How is 'f$(x) =$' different from '$y =$'?

2 How can we find the **asymptotes** of a function?

We have already addressed the ideas of expressions, equations and identities and there are two more related terms in mathematics that our students will encounter: formula and function. A formula is a type of equation that describes the relationship between particular **variables**, such as the formula for the area of a circle, $A = \pi r^2$, or the formula for the displacement of an object travelling with constant acceleration, $s = ut + \frac{1}{2}at^2$. A function has more specific meaning, as we will now see.

Function notation and transformations

When we apply operations to a variable this is called a *function* of the variable. Functions are first introduced to students in terms of function machines, which might look something like the diagram in Figure 4.21.

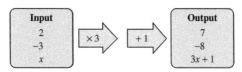

Figure 4.21

The function, f, is represented by the two arrows, so in this example the function is 'multiply by 3 then add 1'. We use the notation f(x), read 'f of x', to show what happens when a function is applied to x; you will already be familiar with many common functions, such as the linear function f$(x) = ax + b$ or the quadratic f$(x) = ax^2 + bx + c$, except that we have so far considered them presented in the form $y = ...$ There is a subtle difference between y, f and f(x): f represents the function to be applied, f(x) represents the function once applied to x, and y represents the output of the function once applied. For this reason it is appropriate to write that $y = $ f(x).

For functions we stick to letters in the middle of the alphabet, so it is not uncommon to see f(x), g(x), h(x) and k(x), although i and j tend to be avoided since they have other important uses, in **complex numbers** and vectors for instance.

Function notation of the form $f(x)$ is particularly powerful as it allows us to show what we're doing with a function very clearly. For any given function, f, we can show that we want to evaluate an input, a, by writing $f(a)$. So if $f(x) = 5x + 6$, then $f(2.5) = 5(2.5) + 6 = 18.5$. On a graph this produces the point (2.5, 18.5).

We can show that we want to find what input gives a particular output, b, by writing $f(x) = b$, so if $f(x) = 2.5$ then $5x + 6 = 2.5$ and $x = \dfrac{2.5 - 6}{5} = -0.7$. On a graph this is the point (−0.7, 2.5).

Even more powerful is the ability to explain how certain functions are related to each other with this notation.

A function $f(x)$ is shown on the graph in Figure 4.22. (To be general, we won't define this function.) The graph shows all the (input, output) pairs that $y = f(x)$ generates.

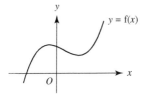

Figure 4.22

If we double all the outputs, the y values are all doubled and we can represent this as $y = 2f(x)$. Since the y values are the distance from the x-axis to the curve, the graph of $y = 2f(x)$ is a vertical stretch of $y = f(x)$ of scale factor 2, where the x-axis remains *invariant* (it's a bit like the entire x-axis is the centre of enlargement): all the distances from the x-axis to the original curve are doubled, as shown in Figure 4.23.

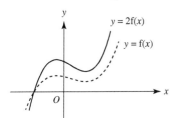

Figure 4.23

Similarly, if we take all our outputs of $f(x)$ and add 2 to each one, this can be represented by $y = f(x) + 2$. Since all the y values will now be 2 higher, the new graph of $y = f(x) + 2$ is a translation of $y = f(x)$ by the vector $\begin{pmatrix} 0 \\ 2 \end{pmatrix}$,

2 places upwards, as shown in Figure 4.24.

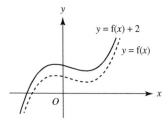

Figure 4.24

Now, if we take all our outputs of $f(x)$ and change their sign, such that 3 becomes -3 or -5.4 becomes 5.4, then this can be represented by $y = -f(x)$. Since all the y values are now their opposite, in terms of sign, the whole graph has been reflected vertically, with the x-axis as the line of symmetry, as in Figure 4.25.

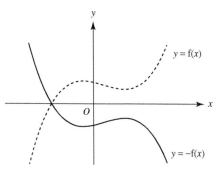

Figure 4.25

So we can see that vertical stretches, translations and reflections can be achieved by transforming the outputs of a function. By transforming the *inputs* of a function, we can achieve horizontal stretches, translations and reflections, but the effects of these can seem counter-intuitive to students at first.

Let's consider what happens when we add 2 to all the x values before they are input into a function. Our function will be $f(x) = x^2$, which has one repeated root at $x = 0$. We'll add 2 to each of the x values before squaring, which means we are also considering the transformed function $f(x+2) = (x+2)^2$. To see the effect of the transformation, we need to compare the resulting graphs directly, so we are interested in which inputs produce the same output. Let's look at a table first.

x	-4	-3	-2	-1	0	1	2	3	4
x^2	16	9	4	1	0	1	4	9	16
$(x+2)^2$	4	1	0	1	4	9	16	25	36

The table makes the effect clear: the values from the second row have all shifted two places to the left to produce the third row. The graphs of $f(x)$ and $f(x + 2)$ are shown on the same axes in Figure 4.26.

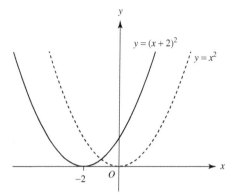

Figure 4.26

So $f(x + 2)$ translates the graph of $f(x)$ two places to the left, by the vector $\begin{pmatrix} -2 \\ 0 \end{pmatrix}$, even though most people's initial thought would be that adding 2 will move it two places to the right. You can think of it as though, coming along the x-axis from $-\infty$ towards 0, the graph of $f(x + 2)$ reaches certain y values *before* the graph of $f(x)$ gets there – as if it had a head start – and then the translation left instead of right makes more sense. Encouraging students to consider the **roots** of the graph helps with this concept: $(x + 2)^2 = 0$ has a solution at $x = -2$, which shows that the vertex of the graph is two places to the left of the vertex of $y = x^2$.

Multiplying x by a constant such as 2 before applying the function has a similarly confusing effect. Students often think that this will produce a horizontal stretch by 2, when in fact the scale factor of the stretch is the **reciprocal** of 2, that is, $\frac{1}{2}$. A table of values can illustrate why this is so.

x	-4	-3	-2	-1	0	1	2	3	4
x^2	16	9	4	1	0	1	4	9	16
$(2x)^2$	64	36	16	4	0	4	16	36	64

Since each x value is doubled before squaring, the function $f(2x)$ reaches higher y values sooner than the original, and so it grows much quicker. This has the graphical effect of a stretch horizontally, scale factor $\frac{1}{2}$, with the y-axis as the invariant line: all the horizontal distances from the y-axis to the original curve get halved, as shown in Figure 4.27.

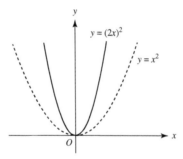

Figure 4.27

Now, if we take all our inputs and change their sign, and then apply the function, we can represent this by $y = f(-x)$. This time, we'll use original function $f(x) = (x+1)^2$ and produce a table of values.

x	-4	-3	-2	-1	0	1	2	3	4
$(x+1)^2$	9	4	1	0	1	4	9	16	25
$(-x+1)^2$	25	16	9	4	1	0	1	4	9

It is clear from the table that the direction of row 2 is reversed to give row 3. This produces a horizontal reflection with the y-axis as the line of reflection, as in Figure 4.28.

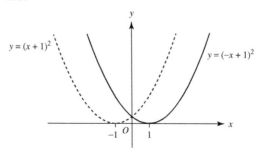

Figure 4.28

For the previous example we looked at $f(x) = (x+1)^2$ instead of $f(x) = x^2$. Why was it not a good idea to use the latter?

 Discuss

Transforming functions can be a very tricky topic for students. What examples and explanations do your colleagues use that have proved particularly effective?

A summary of all the transformations can be seen in the table.

Vertical transformations (affecting the output)		Horizontal transformations (affecting the input)	
$f(x)+a$	translation by $\begin{pmatrix} 0 \\ a \end{pmatrix}$	$f(x+a)$	translation by $\begin{pmatrix} -a \\ 0 \end{pmatrix}$
$af(x)$	stretch by scale factor a	$f(ax)$	stretch by scale factor $\dfrac{1}{a}$
$-f(x)$	reflection in the x-axis	$f(-x)$	reflection in the y-axis

 4.2a Preparing to teach – do the mathematics!

Try these questions yourself before proceeding

1 *Even* functions are those where $f(x) = f(-x)$; *odd* functions are those where $f(x) = -f(-x)$. How do each of these properties look on a graph? What functions do we meet in school mathematics that have these properties?

2 The function $g(x) = x^2$ is transformed to the function $g(3x-2)+1 = (3x-2)^2+1$. What are the transformations that take place? Must they be performed in a particular order? Justify your answer.

Inverse and composite functions

An **inverse** function, written $f^{-1}(x)$, reverses the effect of a function, so it takes the outputs of $f(x)$ and returns the original inputs. Some inverse functions are quite clear. If $f(x) = 5x$, then $f^{-1}(x) = \dfrac{x}{5}$; if $g(x) = x^3$, then $g^{-1}(x) = \sqrt[3]{x}$. Some require more thought. The general process to find an inverse function is:

$f(x) = \dfrac{2x+1}{3-x}$ so $y = \dfrac{2x+1}{3-x}$ Write $y = \ldots$

$x = \dfrac{2y+1}{3-y}$ Switch y with x.

$3x - xy = 2y + 1$

$2y + xy = 3x - 1$ Make y the subject to find the inverse function.

$y(x+2) = 3x - 1$

$y = \dfrac{3x-1}{x+2}$

$f^{-1}(x) = \dfrac{3x-1}{x+2}$

Interestingly, a function and its inverse are always reflections of each other in the line $y = x$, as shown for the previous example in Figure 4.29.

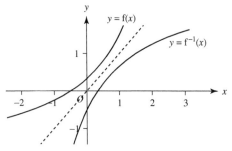

Figure 4.29

If I were to take an x value, apply a function f to it, then apply a function g to the output, the function that would get me in one step from my original input to my final output is the **composite** function $g(f(x))$ or $gf(x)$. This function can be found by substituting the whole of $f(x)$ for x in $g(x)$.

For instance, if $f(x) = 3x - 2$ and $g(x) = x^3$, then $gf(x) = (3x - 2)^3$ and $fg(x) = 3x^3 - 2$.

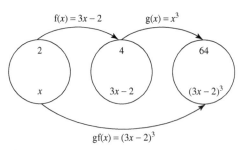

Figure 4.30

 Thinking about the classroom

Students find it tricky to compose functions, and are often unsure which way to perform the composition: does $gf(x)$ mean f goes into g or g goes into f? Writing extra brackets can help to show that $g(f(x))$ means substitute $f(x)$ into $g(x)$. Practise substituting numbers *and* whole expressions into functions before starting to compose functions.

It can help to draw diagrams like the one in Figure 4.30 to illustrate what happens when we substitute one function into another.

Sketching polynomials and finding roots

We talked about cubic functions in Section 2.1, where we noted that they have up to three roots and mentioned that there is a formula to find these, although it is ridiculously complex compared to the equations themselves. The graph of $y = x^3$ is shown in Figure 4.31.

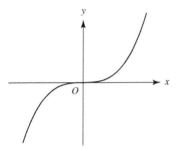

Figure 4.31

Other cubics can have more peaks and troughs (called maxima and minima). Take the cubic $f(x) = x^3 - 2x^2 - 3x$, which can be **factorised** to find its roots.

$$y = x^3 - 2x^2 - 3x$$
$$= x(x^2 - 2x - 3)$$
$$= x(x - 3)(x + 1)$$

The equation $f(x) = 0$ therefore has solutions $x = 0$, $x = 3$ and $x = -1$; the graph is shown in Figure 4.32.

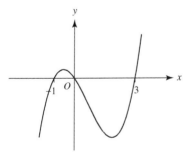

Figure 4.32

A repeated root, just like with a quadratic, is a point where the graph skims the x-axis – where the axis is **tangent** to the graph. For instance, the graph of $y = (2x+3)^2(1-x)$, shown in Figure 4.33, has a repeated root at $x = -\dfrac{3}{2}$.

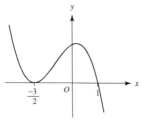

Figure 4.33

Some higher-order **polynomials** continue to be named: one of degree 4 is a quartic, of degree 5 is a quintic, of degree 6 is a sextic, of degree 7 (rather unfortunately) is a septic. It is more common, however, to use the phrase 'polynomial of degree …' after about quintic. It has been suggested that a polynomial of degree 100 be called a *hectic*, although this is rather inconsistent, etymologically speaking. All the other -*tics* have prefixes deriving from Latin, and you will recognise many of them from other words. The Latin prefix for one hundred is *cent*- as in *century* or *centimetre*, but we do not have a *centic*. The *hec*- prefix could come from the Greek *hekaton*, meaning one hundred, as we use in the word *hectare*, but the change in root language here is odd. Perhaps someone chose it deliberately to convey the feeling you might have when working with a polynomial of degree 100!

The number of roots of each polynomial corresponds to its degree: a polynomial of degree n will have exactly n roots. Some may be real, some complex.[3] This is such an important idea that it is called the fundamental theorem of algebra (we mentioned this in Section 2.3). Sometimes a root will be repeated (its **multiplicity** will be greater than 1), sometimes there will be fewer than n real roots, as in the case of a quadratic that doesn't pass through the x-axis at all, or the cubic $y = x^3 + 2x^2 + 4$, seen in Figure 4.34, in which case the remaining roots are complex.

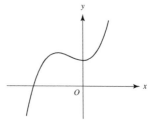

Figure 4.34

---

[3] Although, being accurate, real numbers *are* complex. Here we are pointing out that a polynomial of degree n will have n complex roots, and up to n of them may be purely real.

In order to sketch these polynomials we need to know where they intercept the x-axis ($y = 0$) and the y-axis ($x = 0$). We also need to consider where any turning points (maxima and minima) are. On a quadratic we have two ways to find the single turning point: complete the square to get the coordinates of this point or use the **parabola's** symmetry to find the x value halfway between the roots.

On a higher-order polynomial we need to consider the leading term (the ax^n term in a polynomial of degree n) to know the general shape. The table in Figure 4.35 illustrates the general shape of a quadratic, cubic, quartic and quintic, and what difference a positive or negative leading term makes.

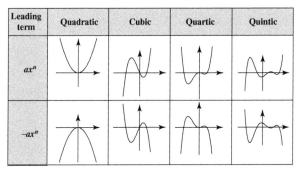

Figure 4.35

If a polynomial won't factorise, and if you don't have a general formula for solving $f(x) = 0$ algebraically, such as the quadratic formula, then other methods are needed for finding roots. Such methods are called numerical methods and employ iteration – they are techniques that, when applied repeatedly, home in on a root.

One of the most straightforward iterative methods is to take an equation and rewrite it so that x is both the subject *and* on the other side of the equals sign. We then turn our resulting equation into an iterative formula and use this to find the root. This is best illustrated with an example, so we are going to find the only root of $f(x) = x^3 - 2x + 5$ which, as you can see in the graph in Figure 4.36, is just less than −2.

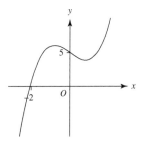

Figure 4.36

Since we are finding the solution to $f(x) = 0$ we set the cubic equal to 0 and try a rearrangement.

$$x^3 - 2x + 5 = 0$$
$$x^3 = 2x - 5$$
$$x = \sqrt[3]{2x - 5}$$

This equation represents the solution of two simultaneous equations: the intersection of the line $y = x$ and the curve $y = \sqrt[3]{2x - 5}$, which are solved by substituting x for y in the second equation.

Writing this rearrangement in iterative form (that is, the same form as the recurrence relations we saw in Section 4.1) gives:

$$x_{n+1} = \sqrt[3]{2x_n - 5}$$

We can then take a starting value, x_0, substitute it in to generate x_1, use that to find x_2, and so on until the sequence of values we generate converges to a limit, that limit being our root in question.

Let's pick $x_0 = -1$ and generate the sequence (on most modern calculators you can use the ANS key to do this process very quickly). Successive iterations give:

$$x_0 = -1$$
$$x_1 = -1.91293$$
$$x_2 = -2.06658$$
$$x_3 = -2.09029$$
$$x_4 = -2.09390$$
$$x_5 = -2.09445$$
$$x_6 = -2.09453$$
$$x_7 = -2.09454$$
$$x_8 = -2.09455$$
$$x_9 = -2.09455$$

and from this we can see that the root is -2.095 (to 3 d.p.).

On the diagram in Figure 4.37 we can see how this process works. The graphs of $y = x$ and $y = \sqrt[3]{2x - 5}$ are shown, and you can follow the arrows on the 'staircase' to see how the root is found.

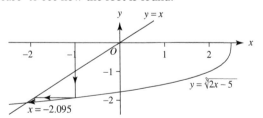

Figure 4.37

4.2b Preparing to teach – do the mathematics!

Try this question yourself before proceeding

Not all rearrangements produce a root. First, show how we can rearrange $x^3 - 2x + 5 = 0$ to $x = \dfrac{2x - 5}{x^2}$ and $x = \dfrac{x^3 + 5}{2}$. Do either of these rearrangements help you to find the root using $x_0 = -2$? Show graphically why they do/don't work.

For those that don't work, is there an x_0 that would produce a root using this iterative formula?

Graphs of circles

The equation of a graph, as we know, is the formula that links all the x and y values that lie on the graph. A circle is particularly interesting in this respect. If we take a circle of radius r, which is centred at $(0, 0)$, and pick a general point (x, y) on the circumference of the circle then, given that x is the horizontal distance from the origin and y the vertical distance, x and y are linked by Pythagoras' theorem.

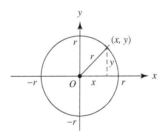

Figure 4.38

So we have that $x^2 + y^2 = r^2$, which is the equation of the circle. If we change the centre of the circle to (h, k) then we can see how this affects our application of Pythagoras' theorem.

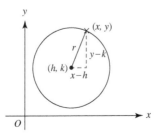

Figure 4.39

This gives us the general equation of a circle as $(x-h)^2 + (y-k)^2 = r^2$. Take a moment to convince yourself why, in the context of transforming graphs, this equation would move the centre of the circle from $(0, 0)$ to (h, k).

 Further exploration

In more advanced mathematics, we teach calculus – differentiation and integration. Differentiation can be used to find and classify the turning points on a curve, which fall into three categories: maximum, minimum or point of inflexion. This, combined with the location of the roots and the y-intercept, enables you to sketch quite accurate graphs.

There are other (some far more effective) numerical and iterative methods for solving equations. Interval bisection and the Newton–Raphson method are two good places to start.

The fundamental theorem of algebra allows us to proceed further to find all the complex roots of a polynomial equation. Interestingly, purely complex roots always come in pairs, which will tell you something about the number of real roots an even-degree polynomial and an odd-degree polynomial can have. We have met the fundamental theorems of arithmetic and algebra, but other fields of mathematics have their own fundamental theorems, including calculus and linear programming, which are both mentioned in this book.

The equation of a circle with radius 1, $(x-h)^2 + (y-k)^2 = 1$, can be adapted through stretches to create the more general equation of an ellipse, $\dfrac{(x-h)^2}{a^2} + \dfrac{(y-k)^2}{b^2} = 1$, where a and b are the horizontal and vertical radii of the ellipse. This shape, along with the circle, parabola and hyperbola, can be created by slicing a cone in different ways and, as such, they are called *conic sections*. The mathematics surrounding these sections, the curves, and the different ways of defining them is fascinating.

Asymptotic behaviours and illegal moves

Some functions have very interesting behaviours around certain inputs. Take, for instance, $f(x) = \dfrac{1}{x}$ and substitute in $x = 0$. What is $\dfrac{1}{0}$? How many zeros are there in 1? You could argue that there are infinitely many zeros in 1, which is understandable, so we could write a statement using the 'tends to' symbol, $\rightarrow$, such as 'As $x \rightarrow 0$, $\dfrac{1}{x} \rightarrow \infty$.' But this is problematic. Dividing by zero is problematic.

If $y = \dfrac{1}{0}$ it would be fair to write $y \times 0 = 1$, but there is no number that can be multiplied by 0 to make 1. This means our original statement must be some kind of mathematically illegal move, so we say that division by zero is 'undefined'. Incidentally, dividing 0 by 0 is awkward in a slightly different way. If $a = \dfrac{0}{0}$ then $a \times 0 = 0$, but there are infinitely many solutions to this equation, which adds more to the undefined nature of dividing by zero.

Back to our function $f(x) = \dfrac{1}{x}$. If we produce a table of values with x approaching zero from both directions, we see the following.

x	-1	-0.1	-0.01	-0.001	0	0.001	0.01	0.1	1
$\dfrac{1}{x}$	-1	-10	-100	-1000	undefined	1000	100	10	1

The next problematic thing is that $\dfrac{1}{x} \to \infty$ as x approaches zero from the right, but $\dfrac{1}{x} \to -\infty$ as x approaches zero from the left. This further adds to the undefined nature of dividing by zero; it appears that the 'answer' can be simultaneously infinitely positive *and* infinitely negative.

The graph of $y = \dfrac{1}{x}$ is shown in Figure 4.40.

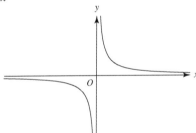

Figure 4.40

The x-axis and y-axis are lines the graph approaches but will never meet; they are called asymptotes (from the Greek *asumptotos*, which means 'not falling together'). The family of graphs related to $y = \dfrac{1}{x}$ are called reciprocal graphs and can be created with all the transformations we've met so far.

 Thinking about the classroom

Students find it difficult to identify transformations of reciprocal graphs. This often comes down to their ability to work with fractions. Substituting $x + 2$ into $f(x) = \dfrac{1}{x}$ gives $\dfrac{1}{x+2}$, leading us to understand that the fraction bar implies the presence of brackets, helping us to recognise that this is $f(x+2)$ rather than $f(x)+2$, that is, a horizontal translation rather than a vertical translation.

A vertical stretch of $2f(x)$ is $2 \times \dfrac{1}{x} = \dfrac{2}{x}$, but $\dfrac{1}{2x}$ could be either horizontal or vertical. $\dfrac{1}{2}f(x) = \dfrac{1}{2} \times \dfrac{1}{x} = \dfrac{1}{2x}$ but $f(2x)$ would look exactly the same. Since the graph of $y = \dfrac{1}{x}$ is symmetrical about both the x- and y-axes, both the horizontal and vertical transformations have the same effect. For this reason you need to pick the functions you use carefully when demonstrating transformations of functions.

There are other functions that have asymptotic behaviours. Let's consider exponential functions for a moment. We've already looked at these in Section 1.3, when we discovered the exponential constant, e, in Section 3.1, where we considered compound interest, and at the start of Chapter 4, when we looked at geometric sequences. An exponential function is of the form $f(x) = a^x$, where $a > 0$. When $a > 1$, all exponential functions have a very similar shape; as x gets more negative the outputs get closer to zero, since negative **indices** reciprocate the **base**. Three examples are shown in the following table, which gives (x, y) pairs for the exponential functions 2^x, 5.5^x and 10^x, with corresponding graphs in Figure 4.41.

x	-10	-5	-1	0	1	2	3
2^x	$\dfrac{1}{1024}$	$\dfrac{1}{32}$	$\dfrac{1}{2}$	1	2	4	8
5.5^x	$0.000\,000\,039$	$0.000\,199$	$\dfrac{2}{11}$	1	5.5	30.25	166.375
10^x	$0.000\,000\,000\,1$	$0.000\,01$	0.1	1	10	100	1000

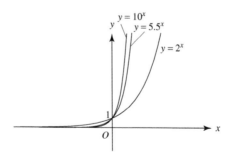

Figure 4.41

When the base is between 0 and 1 we can make a clever adjustment to see what the graphs will look like. Take $\left(\frac{1}{2}\right)^x$ and use the laws of indices (Section 1.3) such that $\left(\frac{1}{2}\right)^x = \left(2^{-1}\right)^x = 2^{-x}$. If $f(x) = 2^x$ then $f(-x) = 2^{-x} = \left(\frac{1}{2}\right)^x$, meaning that the graph of $y = \left(\frac{1}{2}\right)^x$ is a reflection of $y = 2^x$ in the y-axis and, more generally, the graph of $y = \left(\frac{1}{a}\right)^x$ is a reflection of $y = a^x$ in the y-axis.

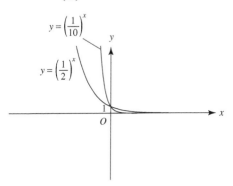

Figure 4.42

For any value of $a > 0$, except when $a = 1$, the function $f(x) = a^x$ approaches zero but never gets there (take a moment to consider why this behaviour is not shown when $a = 1$), so the x-axis is an asymptote. Once we start to transform these functions the asymptote can change location.

 4.2c Preparing to teach – do the mathematics!

Try these questions yourself before proceeding

1 We have looked at six transformations of functions: $kf(x)$, $f(kx)$, $f(x) + k$, $f(x + k)$, $-f(x)$ and $f(-x)$, where k is a constant. Which of these would change the location of the asymptote of $f(x) = a^x$?

2 We defined exponential functions such that the base had to be a positive number. Why can the base not be negative? What would a graph of $y = (-a)^x$ look like?

In Section 1.3 we met, in the context of a fictitious investment, the exponential constant, e, which is an irrational number approximated to 2.718. It is sometimes called Euler's constant and one of the most important constants in mathematics alongside 1, 0, π and i. This number is also called the *natural exponential base*, and $f(x) = e^x$ is the natural exponential function or simply *the* exponential function.[4] Due to the similarities in shape of every exponential function, $y = e^x$ can be transformed to fit any other exponential function, $y = a^x$. For this reason, any model that uses exponential growth or decay can be set up using e^x; examples of this include population growth in biology or financial growth in economics.

 Further exploration

The exponential function appears throughout mathematics. We can use it, along with the imaginary constant, i, to create expressions equivalent to the trigonometric functions sin x, cos x and tan x. It is found in probability theory when analysing the probability of certain events using the Poisson distribution and it is intrinsic to the solution of differential equations, which are the equations used in mathematical models that consider the rate of change of variables.

 Thinking about the classroom

It is important that our students become proficient in sketching and transforming the following graphs: linear, quadratic, cubic, exponential and reciprocal (as well as the trigonometric graphs of sine, cosine and tangent, although we won't go into these here). Students tend to struggle with graphs. It's not unusual to hear, 'I hate graphs!', which in most cases comes down to either a lack of understanding of what a graph actually is (and therefore why they are so very useful), or a lack of proficiency in recognising the shape and features of different types of graph. Never underestimate the amount of work students need on graphs compared with other areas of the curriculum!

In order to sketch graphs of any function there is a useful checklist to run through:

1. What is the general shape?
2. What happens as $x \to \infty$ or as $x \to -\infty$?
3. Where does the graph cross the y-axis? (Solve $x = 0$.)
4. Where does the graph cross the x-axis? (Solve $y = 0$.)
5. Are there any asymptotes? Where are they?

Following a checklist can be very helpful to students in many topics, especially when there are a lot of aspects to consider. Once the students are more familiar with the process at hand, their reliance on the list will diminish.

---

[4] The significant property of this function is to do with calculus, differentiation specifically. When exponential functions are differentiated they become other exponential functions. $f(x) = e^x$ is the special exponential function that, when differentiated, becomes itself.

Discuss

What other types of problem or question involve a lot of steps that could be broken down into a reliable list to follow? How could you gradually reduce students' reliance on the list?

Gradients and areas

The gradient of a function is one of the most important concepts in mathematics. It is a measure of how the function is changing. For instance, on a distance–time graph, where time is plotted along the x-axis and distance travelled is plotted along the y-axis, the gradient calculated by $\frac{\Delta y}{\Delta x}$ (see Section 2.3) measures $\frac{\text{change in distance}}{\text{change in time}}$, which is the speed of travel. Linking the calculation to its associated units can make this idea clearer: $\frac{\text{change in metres}}{\text{change in seconds}}$ implies $\frac{\text{m}}{\text{s}}$ or m s^{-1}, which is a measure of speed.

A straight line signifies constant speed, whereas a curved line shows a changing speed: acceleration or deceleration. To measure the speed at a point in time on a curved line, we must find the gradient of the curve *at that instant*. To find the gradient of a curve at a particular point we must, in fact, find the gradient of the tangent to the curve at that point.

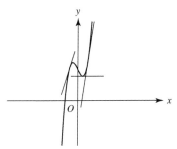

Figure 4.43

Differentiation allows us to precisely find the gradient of the tangent to a curve at any point, but without differentiation we can estimate this gradient by drawing a tangent line and calculating the gradient of our drawn line. Although this process is quite straightforward, interpreting the meaning of the gradient can be more troublesome. Consider a velocity–time graph, where time is plotted along the x-axis and velocity is plotted along the y-axis. Here the gradient measures $\frac{\text{change in velocity}}{\text{change in time}}$ or $\frac{\text{m s}^{-1}}{\text{s}} = \frac{\text{m}}{\text{s}^2}$ or m s^{-2}, which is the change in velocity per unit time, or the acceleration.

The rate at which a quantity is changing, or the gradient of the curve, is essential as it describes *how* a change is taking place, rather than just observing the change. It is this insight that makes many mathematical models in areas such as science and economics so very powerful.

Hand-in-hand with the gradient of a curve goes the area under a curve. In the realms of calculus, where differentiation finds the gradient, it is integration that (while being the reverse of differentiation and therefore essential in solving differential equations) finds the area under a curve. One very simple application of this can be seen in a velocity–time graph, where the area under the curve represents the distance travelled. Without integration, this area can be estimated, and there are methods of varying effectiveness to do this. Aside from variants on 'counting squares', a more accurate method of estimating area is called the *trapezium rule*, which works by dividing a given area into trapezia of equal width.

Take the curve in Figure 4.44, with equation $y = \frac{1}{2}x^3 - 5x^2 + 12x$, where we will estimate the area under the curve between $x = 1$ and $x = 4$. By dividing the area into three trapezia, each of width 1, we can find an estimate for the area; note that this is an underestimate due to the white space between the top of the trapezia and the curve. If we use more trapezia of smaller width our estimate improves.

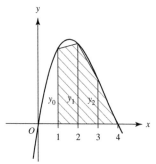

Figure 4.44

We call the lengths of the parallel sides of the trapezia y_0, y_1, y_2, etc., the constant width of each trapezium is h and the number of trapezia is n. This gives the area (using the formula for the area of a trapezium, $\frac{1}{2}(a+b)h$, where a and b are the parallel sides).

$$\text{Area} \approx \frac{1}{2}(y_0 + y_1)h + \frac{1}{2}(y_1 + y_2)h + \frac{1}{2}(y_2 + y_3)h + \cdots + \frac{1}{2}(y_{n-1} + y_n)h$$
$$\approx \frac{1}{2}h[y_0 + y_1 + y_1 + y_2 + y_2 + \cdots + y_{n-1} + y_{n-1} + y_n]$$
$$\approx \frac{1}{2}h[y_0 + y_n + 2(y_1 + \cdots + y_{n-1})]$$

Here you will notice that all the heights are used twice apart from the first and last, hence the **multiple** of 2 in the simplified formula.

We can calculate each of the heights by substituting the relevant x-coordinate into the equation of the curve to find the y-coordinate. So for our example curve with three strips from $x = 1$ to $x = 4$, we have:

$$\text{Area} \approx \frac{1}{2} \times 1 \times [7.5 + 0 + 2(8 + 4.5)]$$
$$\approx 16.25$$

As with most formulae, there are plenty of places for mistakes to be made, not least in the **substitution**. It is important that students know very clearly which part of the formula represents the height and the width of the trapezia, which values are doubled (or not), and how to find the heights.

 Further exploration

Calculus begins with the concepts we have just started to discuss and is one of the bedrocks of mathematics. It is testament to the breadth of our subject that we can study it for a decade or so before we even meet one of its most fundamental ideas, but when we get there a new world is revealed.

In the vein of Hippasus, irrational numbers and the muddy underbelly of mathematics, the story of calculus isn't without its drama (although this one is not so murderous). Sir Isaac Newton and the German Gottfried Wilhelm Leibniz found themselves embroiled in a longstanding feud over who was the first to discover calculus, with Newton accusing Leibniz of stealing his ideas. It is Leibniz to whom we accredit our modern notation and the name calculus (Newton called his discovery the *method of fluxions*). The feud was 'settled' at the time by a report in Newton's favour, produced by the Royal Society but written by Newton himself – hardly independent. Scholars are still undecided as to who first discovered what and how much each man's work influenced the other.

It is with calculus that we meet one of the early influential women in mathematics. The first ever comprehensive book on both differentiation and integration was written by the Italian mathematician Maria Gaetana Agnesi, who incidentally was, in 1750, one of the first women to gain a professorship at a European university. The influence of women in mathematics has gradually increased over the centuries and there are some very good books available on this topic, especially if you are looking for female mathematical role models for your students.

More on inequalities

Quadratic inequalities

We looked at linear **inequalities** in Section 2.2, but there are some special considerations to be made when dealing with quadratic inequalities, and some very common errors that students make. Consider the equation:

$$x^2 - 12x + 32 = 0$$
$$(x - 8)(x - 4) = 0$$
$$x = 8 \text{ or } x = 4$$

What would happen if the equation was changed to an **inequality** such as $x^2 - 12x + 32 < 0$? Many students write that $x < 8$ or $x < 4$ which, when you stop to think, is a bizarre statement, since $4 < 8$. Drawing a graph like that in Figure 4.45 helps us to see more clearly what is going on.

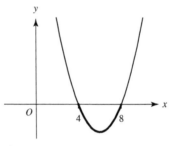

Figure 4.45

We can see that the graph is below zero when $4 < x < 8$, so this is the correct solution to the inequality, telling us that any number that is greater than 4 and at the same time less than 8 is a solution.

If we reverse the direction of the inequality symbol, to give $x^2 - 12x + 32 > 0$, then we are interested in the sections of the graph highlighted in Figure 4.46.

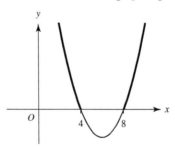

Figure 4.46

There are two disjoint sets of numbers here that satisfy the inequalities: $x < 4$ or $x > 8$. These must be written as two separate sets and not as $4 > x > 8$, as some students try to do, since any number less than 4 or *alternatively* greater than 8 is a solution.

Inequalities with two variables

Sometimes inequalities compare two variables, y and x, instead of just one, and these can be visualised as a region on a graph, instead of as a section on a number line. For instance, the line $y = 3 - x$ tells us all the pairs of numbers, (x, y), where the y value is x less than 3. The inequality $y < 3 - x$ indicates the region below this line, and $y > 3 - x$ indicates the region above, as shown in Figure 4.47.

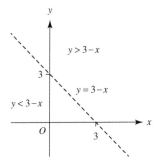

Figure 4.47

To show that a line is included in the region, such as $y \leq 3 - x$, we draw it solid; and to show that it is not included, such as $y < 3 - x$, we draw it dashed.

Identifying the correct region can be confusing for students. If $7 \geq x + y$ do we need the region above the line? If $x - y < 5$ do we need the region below? One way to check is to test a point, say $(0, 0)$, in the inequality. If this point produces a true statement, it is in the correct region. Another way is to make y the subject of the inequality. If it reads $y < \ldots$ then we want the region below the line, and if it reads $y > \ldots$ then we want the region above the line.

Solving systems of inequalities has a particular application in decision mathematics – the branch of mathematics concerned with optimisation – where we use inequalities in a process called *linear programming*. To illustrate the process, let's imagine a fictitious company that manufactures mathematical sweets. The company currently makes two packets of sweets: the 'Euler bag', with sweets shaped like e, i, π, 1, 0; and the 'Ramanujan bag', with all the digits from 1 to 9 and lots of square root symbols. The Euler bag sells for £3.00 and takes 1 minute to pack and the Ramanujan bag sells for £3.50, taking 1.5 minutes to pack. There are 20 available hours (or 1200 minutes) in the week for making packets of sweets, and there are enough ingredients to make 1000 bags altogether. How many of each bag should the company make to maximise their takings?

We can model this as a linear programming problem.

Let x be the number of Euler bags and y be the number of Ramanujan bags.

Maximise $T = 3x + 3.5y$ subject to the constraints:

$$x + 1.5y \leq 1200$$
$$x + y \leq 1000$$
$$x \geq 0, \quad y \geq 0$$

If we mark all of these regions on a graph, leaving the region we want unshaded, we get the graph in Figure 4.48.

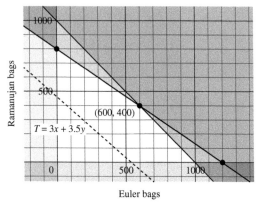

Figure 4.48

Any point (x, y) in the white region, called the feasible region, represents a possible number of each bag of sweets that could be manufactured, but it is the point (600, 400) that is the optimal point. If the company makes 600 Euler bags and 400 Ramanujan bags they will get the greatest takings, of $T = 600 \times 3 + 400 \times 3.5 = £3200$, assuming they sell everything. Any other combination will result in less money.

 Further exploration

In the previous example, the graphical linear programming process involves considering a family of lines parallel to the line given by $T = 3x + 3.5y$ (which is called the 'objective function'). How the optimal point is reached is the fundamental theorem of linear programming, which says the optimal point will be one of the vertices of the feasible region. When there are more than two variables involved, a graph won't work and we need another method. This is where something called the Simplex method comes in.

Decision mathematics is all about maximising and minimising (profit, wastage, time, effort), and creating algorithms to complete processes efficiently. It is employed in computing and business, and is one of the most recently developed branches of mathematics that is studied in schools.

4.3 Proof

 Try this first

1 If I add together two **prime** numbers, such as 13 and 29, the answer is even. Is this always true? How do I know?

2 How many different types of proof can you name?

If I take three consecutive **natural numbers** and sum them up, something interesting happens. For instance, $1 + 2 + 3 = 6$, $10 + 11 + 12 = 33$, $1237 + 1238 + 1239 = 3714$. It appears that the answer is always a multiple of 3. An interested student might test this out a handful of times, a whole class of students might each test it out a handful of times, and all will discover that every answer they reach is indeed a multiple of 3. This might be enough to convince them that this will always happen, no matter which numbers they pick, but unless they were to continue forever, testing all sets of three consecutive numbers, how do they *know* they won't find a **counterexample** – the one set that doesn't play along? Mathematics is full of results that seem true, but unless we can prove absolutely that something will always work, then what we have is merely a **conjecture**. Once something is proven to always be true it can be called a **theorem**.

It turns out that some results are very easy to prove. Take our three consecutive numbers, for instance. If I call the first one n (and stipulate that n can be *any* natural number), then the next number along is $n + 1$, and the next $n + 2$. When we sum these three numbers we get:

$$n + (n + 1) + (n + 2) = 3n + 3 = 3(n + 1)$$

The answer has been shown to be a multiple of 3, regardless of the starting number (and, more precisely, the answer is 3 lots of the middle number), and we have formulated an algebraic proof. This is an example of a **proof by deduction**, where we take what we are given and follow logical steps to reach an undeniable conclusion. To be a proper proof we would need to set it out something like this.

Let n, $n + 1$ and $n + 2$ be three consecutive natural numbers. Then their sum is:

$$n + (n + 1) + (n + 2) = 3n + 3$$
$$= 3(n + 1)$$

which is a multiple of 3. Therefore the sum of three consecutive natural numbers is always a multiple of 3.

Students often fail, in cases of proof, to make their work clear and logical (which can stem from a lack of fluency in algebraic manipulation), and to explain their conclusion properly. There is sometimes a strange aversion to writing sentences in mathematics (as many a mathematics teacher has been told, 'You don't write words in mathematics!'). A proof ought to end with a conclusion, explaining what has been demonstrated.

It might be tempting to suggest, as a consequence of the previous result, that the sum of four consecutive integers is a multiple of 4. Some algebraic manipulation shows this not to be the case, but does reveal that the result will be even.

$$n + (n+1) + (n+2) + (n+3) = 4n + 6 = 2(2n+3)$$

If a result is not true, all that is needed is to provide a counterexample – a single example to demonstrate the fallacy. In this case we can see that $1 + 2 + 3 + 4 = 10$, which is not divisible by 4.

There are some standard conventions we use when completing an algebraic proof: n stands for a natural number or an integer (unless you define it otherwise, of course), so $2n$ must be an even number and either $2n+1$ or $2n-1$ must be odd. If we use related numbers, such as consecutive numbers, or consecutive even numbers, then we stick to the same letter in the expression for each. If we use unrelated numbers, then we must use different letters. For instance, to prove that the sum of *any two* odd numbers is always even we could use $2n+1$ and $2m+1$ to represent the odd numbers, giving:

$$(2n+1) + (2m+1) = 2n + 2m + 2 = 2(m+n+1)$$

which must be even since it is a multiple of 2.

Sometimes, we must consider more than one possible case in order to demonstrate a proof, and this is called a **proof by exhaustion**. For instance, we can prove that the sum of the square of a positive integer and the integer itself is always even. The expression $n^2 + n$ represents this situation. We must consider the case that n is even and the case that n is odd, which exhausts all possible types of natural number.

1. When n is even, n^2 is even (since even $\times$ even is even). This means $n^2 + n$ is even + even, which is even.

2. When n is odd, n^2 is odd (since odd $\times$ odd is odd). This means $n^2 + n$ is odd + odd, which is even.

In both cases the expression is even, and so we have proved the statement.[5]

---

[5] In this case there was an alternative approach. If we factorise $n^2 + n$ we get $n(n+1)$, which is the **product** of two consecutive numbers. Since for any two consecutive numbers one will be even and one odd, then their product is always even, since even $\times$ odd is even.

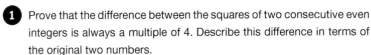

 4.3 Preparing to teach – do the mathematics!

Try these questions yourself before proceeding

1 Prove that the difference between the squares of two consecutive even integers is always a multiple of 4. Describe this difference in terms of the original two numbers.

2 Prove that the difference between the squares of any two odd integers is always a multiple of 8.

It can be quite easy to fool people with a seemingly convincing proof. Take, for instance, this proof that $2 = 1$.

Let $a = b$.	
$a^2 = ab$	Multiply both sides by a.
$a^2 - b^2 = ab - b^2$	Subtract b^2 from both sides.
$(a + b)(a - b) = b(a - b)$	Factorise both sides.
$a + b = b$	Divide both sides by $a - b$.
$a + a = a$	Since $a = b$, substitute a for b.
$2a = a$	Simplify.
$2 = 1$	Divide both sides by a.

In Section 4.2 we looked at the problems with division by zero. How does that affect this proof?

There are other types of mathematical proof, besides deduction and exhaustion. One such method is the **proof by contradiction**, which we used in Section 1.3 to prove that $\sqrt{2}$ is an irrational number, and another is **proof by induction**, which is studied in advanced mathematics courses. As an example of proof by induction, let's prove that the nth term of the triangular numbers (Section 4.1) is indeed $\frac{1}{2}n(n+1)$ (although it is worth pointing out here that this is not the formal way to set out such a proof, rather it is an explanation of the process).

We are going to prove that $u_n = \frac{1}{2}n(n+1)$ for the triangular numbers, using the fact that the first triangular number is 1, the second is $1 + 2$, the third $1 + 2 + 3$, and so on, such that to get from one triangular number to the next you add on consecutive integers.

The first triangular number is 1. Does the formula work when $n = 1$?

$$\frac{1}{2} \times 1 \times (1 + 1) = 1$$

It is clear that the formula is true when $n = 1$.

Now, assume that the formula is true for some general value of n, call it k:

$$u_k = \frac{1}{2}k(k+1)$$

This means the kth triangular number would be $\frac{1}{2}k(k+1)$. The inductive step uses the fact that the next triangular number, the $(k+1)$th number, would be found by adding $k+1$ onto the kth number, so we have:

$$u_{k+1} = u_k + (k+1)$$
$$= \frac{1}{2}k(k+1) + (k+1)$$

Now we factorise $(k+1)$ from both terms to do some clever manipulation:

$$u_{k+1} = \frac{1}{2}k(k+1) + (k+1)$$
$$= \frac{1}{2}(k+1)\{k+2\}$$
$$= \frac{1}{2}(\overline{k+1})\{(\overline{k+1})+1\}$$

Notice that this is strikingly similar to the original formula for u_k, except that k has been replaced with $k+1$, indicated by the **vinculum** above the $k+1$ terms. This leads us to an important conclusion. We assume the formula is true for the kth term, then we work out the $(k+1)$th term from that, and demonstrate in the process that the same formula is true for this $(k+1)$th term. We have then shown that the truth of one term leads to the truth of the next, and so on.

At the start, we showed the formula is true for the first term so, by induction, it is true for the second, then the third, then the fourth, ... In fact, it is true for all n.

The web of mathematics

Proof has proven a thorn in the side of many mathematicians and lots of mathematics over the centuries. One of the most notorious theorems of all time was Fermat's last theorem. Pierre de Fermat was a mathematician in the early seventeenth century who wrote an interesting idea related to Pythagoras' theorem in the margin of one of his textbooks. By Pythagoras' theorem we know that there are infinitely many triplets of natural numbers that satisfy the equation $a^2 + b^2 = c^2$ and that these integers form the three sides of a right-angled triangle.

Fermat conjectured that for any **index** bigger than 2, such as $a^3 + b^3 = c^3$, there are no three positive integers that satisfy the equation. This conjecture gained notoriety since Fermat wrote also that he had 'discovered a truly marvellous proof of this, which this margin is too narrow to contain'.

It turned out that any proof was actually extremely hard to find, and for more than 350 years mathematicians tried, and failed, to prove the result. There are entire books written on the search for a proof, a search that created many new fields of study along the way, and led to Fermat's last theorem being considered by many the hardest problem in mathematics. It wasn't until the mid-1990s that British mathematician Andrew Wiles proved the theorem (at which point it actually became a theorem and not a conjecture).

There are still a number of unproven results in mathematics, which mathematicians are convinced are true but cannot prove. Some of these results are very easy to explain. Consider the twin prime conjecture.

There are infinitely many pairs of primes with a difference of 2.

Or Goldbach's conjecture.

Every even number greater than 2 can be written as the sum of two primes.

Or the Collatz conjecture.

Take any positive integer. If it is even, divide it by 2. If it is odd, multiply it by 3 and add 1. Repeat this process with the result. You will always eventually end up at the number 1.

These results *seem* true – we have found no counterexamples – but they haven't yet been proven.

Some results are much more complex. In the year 2000, the Clay Mathematics Institute, based in the USA, designated their 'Millennium Prize Problems' – a set of seven unproven results that the Institute considered to be the most important in mathematics; they offered a US$1 000 000 prize to anyone who could solve these problems. Only one of them has since been proven. The Poincaré conjecture (which requires a lot of specific knowledge to even understand) was proved in 2003 by the Russian mathematician Grigori Perelman, who used other areas of mathematics to reach his proof. Perelman refused his million-dollar prize, saying that it was unfair for him to accept it when his proof relied so heavily on the work of others.

And that is the thing with mathematics. It is a huge web, where everything is linked and no concept or process stands in isolation from the rest. There are the big foundational ideas at the centre of the web, those that are the root of everything, and we start with many of these at school – arithmetic, proportion, algebra, geometry, statistics, probability, calculus. Many ideas begin by linking up previous ones, and new fields of study are growing the web all the time.

It is our job as mathematics teachers to help our students to access as much of the web as possible. Some of our students will reach their limit in school, others will surpass us, some may even grow the web some more. Whatever the end result, by getting them as far as we can we are allowing them to be a part of one of the most powerful fields of human endeavour, and that is the beauty of being a mathematics teacher.

Quiz 4

1. For the sequence pictured in Figure 4.49, where the staircase grows each time, find the nth term for the number of blocks in a staircase, using a pictorial and an algebraic method.

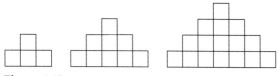

Figure 4.49

2. In Section 4.1 we modelled the sequence $3n+1$ using sticks, as shown in Figure 4.50.

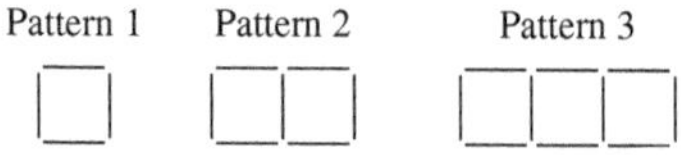

Pattern 1   Pattern 2   Pattern 3

Figure 4.50

In this sequence we are building rectangles with dimensions $1\times n$: 1×1, 1×2, etc. What would the nth term be for a $2\times n$ rectangle? A $3\times n$ rectangle? An $m\times n$ rectangle? What about if we moved into three dimensions with an $m\times n\times p$ cuboid?

3. Given a and b are real numbers, what type of sequence is generated by the following recurrence relations?

   a. $u_{n+1} = au_n$

   b. $u_{n+2} = u_{n+1} + u_n$

   c. $u_{n+1} = u_n + a$

   d. $u_{n+1} = u_n + an + b$

4. $f(x) = x^3$. There are horizontal stretches of $f(x)$ that produce the same graph as vertical stretches of $f(x)$. How can we identify these? More generally, if $g(x) = x^n$, what horizontal and vertical stretches of $g(x)$ produce the same graph?

5. What transformations of $h(x) = x^2$ give the function $k(x) = 9x^2 - 6x + 1$? In what order are these transformations applied?

6. a. Verify that $((a+b)^2 + b^2)((a-b)^2 + b^2) \equiv a^4 + 4b^4$.

The result above is sometimes called *Sophie Germain's identity*. Sophie Germain was a French mathematician from the late eighteenth to early nineteenth century who specialised in, among other things, number theory. She discovered the result, which in itself doesn't appear particularly useful, while working on Fermat's last theorem. It can be exploited when analysing numbers.

b. Hence decide whether or not the number $7^{12} + 2^{2018}$ is prime.

7. How many asymptotes does the function $f(x) = \dfrac{x^3 - 3x^2 + 2x}{x^4 - 16}$ have? What are their equations?

8. If $f(x) = x^2 + 2x + 3$, prove that $f(x) > 0$ for all real values of x.

9. The circle $(x+1)^2 + (y-1)^2 = 1$ has centre $C(-1, 1)$. Explain why the addition of 1 to x and of -1 to y result in a translation by vector $\begin{pmatrix} -1 \\ 1 \end{pmatrix}$ of the circle $x^2 + y^2 = 1$.

10. By considering the graphs of functions and their inverses, what do we know about the point where a function is equal to its inverse, that is, $f(x) = f^{-1}(x)$?

Answers to each Quiz, Try this first *and* Preparing to teach *are at the back of the book.*

Glossary

Below is a, by no means comprehensive, list of useful terms. If a term appears in one part of the book but is explained elsewhere, I have tried to include it here for ease of reference. The first instance in each chapter of a term contained in the glossary is highlighted in bold.

absolute value – The size of a number regardless of its sign. See also **magnitude**.

additive identity – The number you add without changing anything, namely, 0.

additive inverse – The number you add to another to get back to 0.

associativity – The property of addition and multiplication that allows you to perform operations in a different order without reordering the numbers involved, so $(a + b) + c \equiv a + (b + c)$.

asymptote – A line that a graph approaches but never meets.

base – The base of an **exponential** is the number being raised to a power. In 2^3 the base is 2. Since number systems have columnar values that are powers of a particular base, they are named in terms of this base. Our system is base ten.

binomial – A **polynomial** consisting of two **terms**.

binomial expansion – The expansion of a **binomial** raised to a power, such as $(1 + x)^6$.

coefficient – The number that multiplies a letter in a **polynomial**. The coefficient of x^2 in $6 - 4x^2$ is –4.

commutativity – The property of addition and multiplication that allows you to reverse the order of a calculation and get the same answer: $a + b \equiv b + a$.

complex number – A number that is made up of **real** and **imaginary** numbers.

composite – A number that is not prime. Also a function that is the combination of two (or more) others.

conjecture – A mathematical statement believed to be true but not yet proven.

conjugate – The conjugate of a **binomial** is obtained by changing the sign between the terms. The conjugate of $p - q$ is $p + q$.

constant – A number whose value does not change.

continued fraction – A way of writing a number, in the form $a + \cfrac{1}{b + \cfrac{1}{c + \cfrac{1}{d + \dots}}}$.

coprime – Two numbers are coprime when their highest common factor is 1.

counterexample – An example that demonstrates that a statement is false.

cubic – A polynomial of the form $ax^3 + bx^2 + cx + d$.

degree – The degree of a **polynomial** is the highest power of the unknown. The polynomial $x^3 + x^2 - 1$ has degree 3. See also **order**.

difference of two squares – The specific factorisation $x^2 - y^2 \equiv (x - y)(x + y)$.

discriminant – The **expression** that determines the type and number of **roots** of a polynomial equation. A **quadratic equation** has discriminant $b^2 - 4ac$.

distributivity – The property of multiplication/division over addition/subtraction, such that $a(b \pm c) \equiv ab \pm ac$ and $\dfrac{b \pm c}{a} \equiv \dfrac{b}{a} \pm \dfrac{c}{a}$.

dividend – The number to be divided in a division calculation.

divisor – The number to be divided by in a division calculation.

elimination – The process of solving simultaneous equations by transforming them and then combining by adding or subtracting in order to eliminate one of the variables.

equation – A mathematical statement that two **expressions** are equal under certain conditions.

exponent – See **index**.

exponentiation (exponential) – Raising a number to a power, such as 2^3.

expression – A statement involving numbers and variables (letters).

factor – A number that another can be divided by with no remainder.

factorise – Write a number or expression as the product of two or more others.

formula – An equation describing the relationship between certain variables, such as $A = \pi r^2$.

function – An instruction that links a set of inputs with a set of outputs.

gradient – The slope of a line, measuring the vertical increase for every unit of horizontal increase.

identity – A mathematical statement that two **expressions** are always equal.

imaginary number – A number that is a square root of a negative number.

index – The power applied to a number. In 2^3 the index is 3. The plural of index is **indices**. See also **exponent**.

indices – See **index**.

inequality – A mathematical statement that two expressions are not equal to each other, such as $3x - 4 > 7$. An inequality normally has a range of solutions.

integer – A whole number, positive or negative: …, −3, −2, −1, 0, 1, 2, 3, … .

inverse – An operation that undoes the effect of another. The inverse of $+2$ is -2, for instance.

irrational number – A **real number** that cannot be written as a fraction. It has an infinite decimal expansion that does not recur.

like terms – **Terms** that have the same **variables**.

magnitude – See **absolute value**.

minuend – The number to be subtracted from in a subtraction calculation.

multiple – A number that can be made by multiplying another by an integer.

multiplicand – One of the numbers being multiplied in a multiplication calculation.

multiplicative identity – The number you multiply by without changing anything, namely, 1.

multiplicative inverse – The number you multiply by another to get back to 1. See also **reciprocal**.

multiplicity – The number of times a factor is repeated in a factorised number or expression.

natural number – A whole number greater than 0: 1, 2, 3, … .

order – See **degree**.

orthogonal – At right angles. See also **perpendicular**.

parabola – The shape of a **quadratic** graph.

partial denominators – The values a, b, c, d, … in a continued fraction of the form $a + \cfrac{1}{b + \cfrac{1}{c + \cfrac{1}{d + \dots}}}$.

perpendicular – At right angles. See also **orthogonal**.

placeholder – The zeros in a number that ensure other digits hold the correct value.

polynomial – An **expression** consisting of **constants** and **variables** and the operations of addition, subtraction, multiplication (but not division of variables), and non-negative **integer** powers.

prime – A number that has only two distinct **factors**, itself and 1.

product – The answer to a multiplication calculation.

proof by contradiction – A method of proof where something is assumed true, followed through, and a contradiction is reached, invalidating the original assumption.

proof by deduction – A method of proof where we take a mathematical statement and use logical steps to reach a conclusion. Many algebraic proofs fall into this category.

proof by exhaustion – A method of proof where we consider every possible case to show a statement is true.

proof by induction – A method of proof where we show that a statement is true for one case, and that the truth of one guarantees the truth of the next, therefore the statement is true for all cases.

proportional – If two quantities are in proportion, then they are linked by a multiplicative relationship.

quadratic – A polynomial of the form $ax^2 + bx + c$.

quotient – The answer to a division calculation.

radicand – The number inside a square root.

rational number – A number that can be written as a fraction.

rationalising the denominator – The process of making the denominator of a fraction a rational number.

real number – A rational or irrational number.

reciprocal – The reciprocal of n is $\dfrac{1}{n}$.

roots – The roots of an **equation** are where it is equal to 0, the points where the graph crosses the x-axis.

substitution – Replacing **variables** with numerical or algebraic expressions.

subtrahend – The number to be subtracted in a subtraction calculation.

sum – The answer to an addition calculation.

summand – One of the numbers being added in an addition calculation.

surd – A number written in terms of a root.

tangent – A line that just touches, or skims, a curve.

term – The parts of an **expression** separated by addition or subtraction. Also used for a number in a certain position in a sequence.

theorem – A mathematical statement that has been proven to be always true.

unknown – A letter in an **equation** whose value is unknown.

variable – A letter in an **expression** that could take any value.

vinculum – A straight line drawn over an expression to group the terms as a single entity. A vinculum works in a similar way to brackets and can add clarity as expressions become more complex.

Solutions

Chapter 1

Try this first 1.1 (see the body of the text for more detail)

1.

Base 10	1	2	3	4	5	6	7	8	9	10
Base 4	1	2	3	10	11	12	13	20	21	22

2. 0.25 and 0.250 have the same magnitude, but 0.250 is given to a greater degree of accuracy. It may be the result of taking a different number and rounding it to 3 decimal places, or 3 significant figures.

3. The value of each digit changes. Multiplying by 1000 makes each digit 'move' places by three columns to the left, while dividing by 1000 moves each digit three places to the right. Similarly, multiplying by 0.001 moves each digit three places to the right, while dividing by 0.001 moves each digit three places to the left.

1.1a

1. three digits: 0, 1, 2

2. First column: $3^0 = 1$. Second column: $3^1 = 3$. Third column: $3^2 = 9$. nth column: 3^{n-1}.

3. 1, 2, 10, 11, 12, 20, 21, 22, 100, 101

1.1b

To move one, two or three columns to the left, we multiply by 3, 9 or 27, respectively. In ternary, these are written $\times 10$, $\times 100$ or $\times 1000$.

To move one, two or three columns to the right, we multiply by $\dfrac{1}{3}, \dfrac{1}{9}$ or $\dfrac{1}{27}$, respectively. In ternary, these are written $\times 0.1$, $\times 0.01$ or $\times 0.001$.

Try this first 1.2 (see the body of the text for more detail)

1. This is called writing 24 as a product of its prime factors. Since each number has a unique prime factorisation, we can use this form to analyse the properties of numbers.

2. When the minuend is smaller than the subtrahend, you use ten from the next column along in order to avoid negative numbers.

3. If the number's digital sum is divisible by three, then the number itself is also divisible by three. The explanation of this is in the text.

4. * can be replaced by + or ×. This property is called associativity. It does not work with division or subtraction.

1.2a

1. a. commutativity

   b. multiplicative inverse

   c. associativity

   d. commutativity and the additive inverse

   e. distributivity

2. $-2 \div 4(3 + -1) = -2 \div 4 \times 2 = -1$

1.2b

1. Let our two numbers be a and b, and think about a Venn diagram of their prime factors. If we multiply a and b, then we multiply all the prime factors in the a circle by all the prime factors in the b circle. This means we have used the prime factors in the intersection twice. Recall that the LCM of a and b is the product of all visible prime factors in the Venn diagram, and the HCF is the product of the prime factors in the intersection. This means we can multiply the LCM by the HCF and have performed exactly the same calculation as $a \times b$.

2. $24 = 2^3 \times 3$, $36 = 2^2 \times 3^2$, $84 = 2^2 \times 3 \times 7$. For a number to be divisible by 24, 36 and 84 it must contain all their prime factor decompositions. This means that $\text{LCM}(24, 36, 84) = 2^3 \times 3^2 \times 7$. This is not a square number, since some of the indices are odd, but if we multiply it by 2 and 7 then we have the number $2^4 \times 3^2 \times 7^2 = (2^2 \times 3 \times 7)^2 = 84^2 = 7056$.

1.2c

1. Take a five-digit number, n, of the form $abcde$, which can be written:

$$n = 10^4 a + 10^3 b + 10^2 c + 10d + e$$

The rules for divisibility by 10 and 5 go together. The first four terms can be factorised to give $n = 10(10^3 a + 10^2 b + 10^1 c + d) + e$, and the entire number is divisible by 10, if the last digit is also divisible by 10. The only single digit divisible by 10 is 0, which gives us the rule. If we factorise the equation by taking out 5 from the first four terms, we have $n = 5(2000a + 200b + 20c + 2d) + e$, which is divisible by 5, if the last digit is also divisible by 5. The only single digits divisible by 5 are 5 and 0, so we have our rule.

To prove the rule for divisibility by 3 we use the model for divisibility by 9, write each power of 10 as one more than a multiple of 9, but factorise out 3 instead.

$$\begin{aligned} n &= 10^4 a + 10^3 b + 10^2 c + 10d + e \\ &= (9999 + 1)a + (999 + 1)b + (99 + 1)c + (9 + 1)d + e \\ &= 9999a + 999b + 99c + 9d + a + b + c + d + e \\ &= 3(3333a + 333b + 33c + 3d) + a + b + c + d + e \end{aligned}$$

Which shows us that if $a + b + c + d + e$ (that is, the digital sum) is divisible by 3, then so is the entire number.

To prove the rule for divisibility by 8 we use the model for divisibility by 4 and factorise out 8 from as many terms as possible.

$$\begin{aligned} n &= 10^4 a + 10^3 b + 10^2 c + 10d + e \\ &= 8(1250a + 125b) + 100c + 10d + e \end{aligned}$$

This shows that if $100c + 10d + e$ is divisible by 8, then so is the entire number.

$100c + 10d + e$ represents the three-digit number formed by the last three digits c, d and e.

2. Since 6 is the product of 2 and 3, then a proof of the divisibility rules for 2 and 3 is all that is needed to prove divisibility by 6.
3. Checking the divisibility rules for the numbers 1 – 9 we see that it is divisible by all of these numbers.

Try this first 1.3 (see the body of the text for more detail)

1. Fractions whose denominator have a prime factorisation composed of only 2s and 5s produce terminating decimals. If any other prime factors compose the denominator, the fraction produces a recurring decimal. The explanation of this is in the text.

2. $\sqrt{400} = \sqrt{4}\sqrt{100} = 2 \times 10$, so this is an integer. $\sqrt{40000} = \sqrt{400}\sqrt{100} = 20 \times 10$, so this is an integer. However, $\sqrt{40} = \sqrt{4}\sqrt{10} = 2\sqrt{10}$ and $\sqrt{4000} = \sqrt{400}\sqrt{10} = 20\sqrt{10}$, so these are not integers.

3. $\left(\dfrac{125}{27}\right)^{-2/3} = \dfrac{9}{25}$

4. If we multiply the numerator and denominator by $\sqrt{2}$, we get the required equivalent fraction. This form is preferable, as it is a fraction of $\sqrt{2}$, which is easier to work with in other calculations.

181

1.3a

1. By division we can see that $\dfrac{3}{13} = 0.\dot{2}3076\dot{9}$. The repetend is of length 6, so the digit in positions that are a multiple of 6 will be 9, hence the 30th digit after the decimal point is 9.

2. a. $\dfrac{1}{9} = 0.\dot{1}$, with repetend of length 1. $\dfrac{1}{99} = 0.\dot{0}\dot{1}$, with repetend of length 2. $\dfrac{1}{999} = 0.\dot{0}0\dot{1}$, with repetend of length 3. This continues, so $\dfrac{1}{10^n - 1}$ has repetend of length n.

   b. $\dfrac{1}{3}$ has repetend of length 1, and 3 is a factor of 9.

   $\dfrac{1}{7}$ has repetend of length 6, and 7 is a factor of $999\,999$.

   $\dfrac{1}{11}$ has repetend of length 2, and 11 is a factor of 99.

   $\dfrac{1}{13}$ has repetend of length 6, and 13 is a factor of $999\,999$.

   As an extra, take a look at $9 \div 3$, $999\,999 \div 7$, $99 \div 11$ and $999\,999 \div 13$. Why does this happen?

1.3b

1. $(ab)^n \equiv \overbrace{ab \times ab \times ab \times ...}^{n \text{ times}} \equiv \overbrace{a \times a \times a \times ...}^{n \text{ times}} \times \overbrace{b \times b \times b \times ...}^{n \text{ times}} \equiv a^n b^n$. This uses commutativity.

2. $\left(\dfrac{a}{b}\right)^n \equiv \overbrace{\dfrac{a}{b} \times \dfrac{a}{b} \times \dfrac{a}{b} \times ...}^{n \text{ times}} \equiv \dfrac{\overbrace{a \times a \times a \times...}^{n \text{ times}}}{\underbrace{b \times b \times b \times...}_{n \text{ times}}} \equiv \dfrac{a^n}{b^n}$. This is also true for roots, since roots can be expressed as indices.

1.3c

1. This is the particular case of 1.3b question 1, where $n = \dfrac{1}{2}$.

2. This must be done in two parts:

$$\frac{1}{2 + \sqrt{3} - \sqrt{5}} = \frac{1}{(2 + \sqrt{3}) - \sqrt{5}} \times \frac{(2 + \sqrt{3}) + \sqrt{5}}{(2 + \sqrt{3}) + \sqrt{5}}$$

$$= \frac{2 + \sqrt{3} + \sqrt{5}}{2 + 4\sqrt{3}} \times \frac{2 - 4\sqrt{3}}{2 - 4\sqrt{3}}$$

$$\equiv \frac{-8 - 6\sqrt{3} + 2\sqrt{5} - 4\sqrt{15}}{-44}$$

$$= \frac{4 + 3\sqrt{3} - \sqrt{5} + 2\sqrt{15}}{22}$$

1.3d

Assume $\sqrt{3}$ is rational and can be expressed as a fraction in its simplest terms as $\frac{p}{q}$, so p and q are coprime.

$$\sqrt{3} = \frac{p}{q}$$
$$3 = \frac{p^2}{q^2}$$
$$3q^2 = p^2$$

If p^2 is a multiple of 3, then p is also a multiple of 3. Let $p = 3m$. Now we have

$$3q^2 = (3m)^2 = 9m^2$$
$$q^2 = 3m^2$$

So q^2 is a multiple of 3, which means q is a multiple of 3. This means p and q share a common factor of 3, which is a contradiction since we assumed p and q were coprime. This means $\sqrt{3}$ is not a rational number but an irrational one.

Quiz 1

1. A number is an abstract concept of a count or a measurement. Numbers are represented with numerals (e.g. 198, 4.03), which are made up of symbols called digits.

2. a. The first three digits, $7, 8, 5$, are significant. The final 0 is a placeholder.

   b. The first 0 is a placeholder. The three digits 6, 0, 5 are significant.

   c. The first two 0s are placeholders. The last five digits, 2, 5, 0, 3, 0, are significant.

   d. The first four digits, $4, 0, 9, 0$, are significant and the last 0 is a placeholder.

3. Express as a product of prime factors and group together prime factors that make 10 (2s and 5s):

$$2^3 \times 3^2 \times 4^5 \times 5^8 \times 6 = 2^3 \times 3^2 \times (2^2)^5 \times 5^8 \times 2 \times 3$$
$$= 2^{14} \times 3^3 \times 5^8$$
$$= (2^8 \times 5^8) \times 2^6 \times 3^3$$
$$= 10^8 \times 2^6 \times 3^3$$

Therefore there are eight zeros at the end of this number.

4. $378\,000 = 2^4 \times 3^3 \times 5^3 \times 7$. Since we can make all the numbers from 2 to 9 using combinations of these prime factors, 378 000 is divisible by all these numbers.

5. $1032 = 2^3 \times 3 \times 43$. Multiply this by $2 \times 3 \times 43$ to get $2^4 \times 3^2 \times 43^2 = (2^2 \times 3 \times 43)^2$. So the smallest number you can multiply 1032 by to get a square number is $2 \times 3 \times 43 = 258$.

6. To be divisible by 15 the number must be divisible by both 3 and 5. This means the last digit must be 5 or 0 and the digital sum must be a multiple of 3. The current digits are 2, 7, 7 and 5, which sum to 21. If the last digit is 0, then the third digit could be 3, 6 or 9. If the last digit is 5, then the third digit could be 1, 4 or 7. Hence there are six ways to make this number divisible by 15.

7. $9^{56} + 9^{55} = 9^{55}(9+1) = 10 \times 9^{55}$, so the last digit is 0.

8. a. -35 is an integer, rational, real and complex number.

    b. 1.7 is a rational, real and complex number.

    c. $\dfrac{4}{5}$ is a rational, real and complex number.

    d. 0 is an integer, rational, real and complex number.

9. $0.8^{-2} = \left(\dfrac{4}{5}\right)^{-2} = \left(\dfrac{5}{4}\right)^{2} = \dfrac{25}{16} = 1.5625$

10. $6^7 + 6^7 + 6^7 + 6^7 + 6^7 + 6^7 = 6 \times 6^7 = 6^8$

11. The three steps are reciprocate, square root and raise to the fifth power. They can be performed in any order (although it's probably better to square root before raising to the fifth power, unless you are adept at finding square roots of very large numbers!).

12. $9^x = 64$

    $(3^2)^x = 64$ so $(3^x)^2 = 64$. Taking the square root of both sides gives $3^x = 8$. Cubing both sides gives $(3^x)^3 = 512$, which is the same as $(3^3)^x = 27^x = 512$. Using this, $27^{2x} = (27^x)^2 = 512^2 = 262\,144$. We can write 27^{2x} in the form 2^n using $512^2 = (2^9)^2 = 2^{18}$, so $n = 18$.

13. Going from the bottom of the fraction:

$$1 + \cfrac{1}{2 + \cfrac{1}{3 + \cfrac{1}{4}}} = 1 + \cfrac{1}{2 + \cfrac{1}{\frac{13}{4}}} = 1 + \cfrac{1}{2 + \frac{4}{13}} = 1 + \cfrac{1}{\frac{30}{13}} = 1 + \frac{13}{30} = \frac{43}{30} = 1.4\dot{3}$$

14. a. $0.25 = \dfrac{1}{4} = 0.01_2$

   b. $0.0625 = \dfrac{1}{16} = 0.0001_2$

   c. $0.3125 = \dfrac{5}{16} = \dfrac{1}{4} + \dfrac{1}{16} = 0.0101_2$

   d. $0.3 = \dfrac{3}{10} = \dfrac{1}{4} + \dfrac{1}{32} + \dfrac{1}{64} + \dfrac{1}{512} + \dfrac{1}{1024} + \ldots = 0.010\ 011\ 001\ 100\ 11\ldots_2 = 0.01\dot{0}01\dot{1}_2$

   (Note this recurs, since only fractions whose denominators are a power of 2 will terminate when working in binary.)

15. a.   11001
          1101 +
        ─────────
        10 0110
         1   1

   b.   11000
           1010 ×
        ─────────
          00000
         110000
        0000000
       11000000
        ─────────
       11110000

   c. 1 $\overset{0}{\cancel{1}}$ $\overset{10}{\cancel{1}}$ $\overset{1}{\cancel{0}}$ $\overset{1}{\cancel{0}}$ $\overset{1}{\cancel{0}}$ 1 0
      1 0 1 0 1 1 1 −
      ───────────────────
      0 0 1 1 0 0 1

   d. $\dfrac{110\cancel{0}\cancel{0}\cancel{0}}{11\cancel{0}\cancel{0}} = \dfrac{1100}{11}$

        0100
      11)1100

Chapter 2

Try this first 2.1 (see the body of the text for more detail)

1. An expression is a mathematical statement involving numbers and/ or letters. An equation is a statement that one expression is equal to another. A formula is an equation describing the relationship between particular variables, such as $C = \pi d$.

2. Factorising is the process of writing an expression as the product of other expressions. It is so called as the expressions involved are necessarily factors of the original. Factorising is useful in any circumstance when

a multiplicative relationship needs to be used, such as solving certain equations or simplifying fractions.

2.1a

Polynomial	Not polynomial
$2x$ (monomial degree 1)	
$pq^3 \times \dfrac{5}{q^{-4}} \equiv 5pq^7$ (monomial degree 8, since we consider the power of both variables)	$3y^{\frac{1}{2}} - 5$
$2x^2 - 7x + 1$ (trinomial degree 2)	$\int \sin t \cos^3 t \, dt$
$(2x-6)(3x+2)^2 \equiv 18x^3 - 30x^2 - 64x - 24$ (quadrinomial degree 3)	

2.1b

Always true	Sometimes true	Never true
$16m^2 \equiv (4m)^2$	$n^2 = 2n$	$3(x+1) \neq 3x + 1$
$3(x+1) \equiv 3x + 3$	$x^2 > 10$	$a - 3 \neq a - 7$
$x^{\frac{1}{2}} \equiv \sqrt{x}$	$n^2 \geq n$	$x^2 + 25 \neq 0$ (Of course, with complex numbers this should really be in the 'sometimes' column. Revealing that knowledge or not depends on your students.)
$pqr \equiv rqp$	$n - 2 = \dfrac{1}{10}$	
	$X + 2 = Y + 2$	
	$a - b = b - a$	

2.1c

1. $x^3 + 2x^2 + 2x + 1$

2. $(3 - x - y)^2 \equiv (3 - (x+y))^2$
   $\equiv 9 - 2 \times 3(x+y) + (x+y)^2$
   $\equiv 9 - 6x - 6y + x^2 + 2xy + y^2$

2.1d

1. $x^4 y^2 - x^4 - x^3 y^2 + x^3 \equiv x^3(xy^2 - x - y^2 + 1)$
   $\equiv x^3(x(y^2 - 1) - (y^2 - 1))$
   $\equiv x^3(y^2 - 1)(x - 1)$
   $\equiv x^3(y - 1)(y + 1)(x - 1)$

2. $1 + 2a + 2b + a^2 + 2ab + b^2 \equiv 1 + 2(a+b) + (a+b)^2$
   $\equiv (1 + (a+b))^2$
   $\equiv (1 + a + b)^2$

Try this first 2.2 (see the body of the text for more detail)

1. Only you can answer this!

2. The statement becomes untrue if we do not. The explanation of this is in the text.

2.2

1. $xy < -2$

2. $yz < 0$

3. $x - y > 3$

4. $\dfrac{x}{z} > 2$

Try this first 2.3 (see the body of the text for more detail)

1. A graph is a pictorial representation of a relationship that holds between pairs of numbers. It helps us to visualise and understand the links between various such relationships.

2. The gradient of a line is the vertical change for every increase of 1 horizontally.

3. Setting the equation equal to 0 enables us to quickly solve it without having to test multiple possible solutions. If the product of two expressions is 0, one of them must be 0.

2.3a

l_1 rearranges to $y = \dfrac{2x - 12}{3}$ and has gradient $\dfrac{2}{3}$, so l_2 has gradient $\dfrac{-3}{2}$. l_1 crosses the x-axis at $x = 6$ (set y to 0 in the equation of the line), so l_2 has equation $y = \dfrac{-3}{2}x + c$ and also passes through the point $(6, 0)$. Using this point we have $0 = \dfrac{-3}{2}(6) + c$, giving $c = 9$. The equation of l_2 is $y = \dfrac{-3}{2}x + 9$, which can also be written as $3x + 2y = 18$.

2.3b

From the quadratic formula, $x = \dfrac{-b \pm \sqrt{b^2 - 4ac}}{2a}$, the rationality or irrationality of the roots depends on the value of $\sqrt{b^2 - 4ac}$. If this is irrational, both roots must be irrational. If this is rational, both roots must be rational. It is impossible for one root to be rational and one irrational.

Try this first 2.4 (see the body of the text for more detail)

1. Simultaneous equations arise when we want to find the value of two (or more) unknowns and we have two (or more) equations to describe the relationship between these unknowns.

2. If we have n unknowns, then we need n equations in order to find the value of these unknowns.

3. The two most common in school are elimination and substitution, but there are others. See the text.

2.4

1. If there are no solutions then the two lines will be parallel.

2. The answer to this question can be seen by considering the solutions to the simultaneous equations arising from each scenario:

Line and cubic: $a_1 x + b_1 = a_2 x^3 + b_2 x^2 + c_2 x + d_2$. This is an equation of degree 3, having up to three real roots, so there are up to three intersections.

Two quadratics: $a_1 x^2 + b_1 x + c_1 = a_2 x^2 + b_2 x + c_2$. This is an equation of degree 2, having up to two real roots, so there are up to two intersections.

Quadratic and cubic: $a_1 x^2 + b_1 x + c_1 = a_2 x^3 + b_2 x^2 + c_2 x + d_2$. This is an equation of degree 3, having up to three real roots, so there are up to three intersections.

mth and nth degree polynomial: Once equated the equation will have degree n (given $n \geq m$), so there are up to n intersections.

Quiz 2

1. $((x+2y)-3z)((x+2y)+3z) \equiv (x+2y)^2 - 9z^2 \equiv x^2 + 4xy + 4y^2 - 9z^2$

2. $(2m-n)(m+2n)(2m+n)(m-2n) \equiv (2m-n)(2m+n)(m+2n)(m-2n)$
$$\equiv (4m^2 - n^2)(m^2 - 4n^2)$$
$$\equiv 4m^4 - 17m^2 n^2 + 4n^4$$

3. $8y^4 - 13y^2 - 6 \equiv 8y^4 - 16y^2 + 3y^2 - 6$
$$\equiv 8y^2(y^2 - 2) + 3(y^2 - 2)$$
$$\equiv (y^2 - 2)(8y^2 + 3)$$

4. The product of the roots is equal to $\dfrac{c}{a}$ so $\dfrac{40}{a} = 8$, giving $a = 5$. The sum of the roots is equal to $\dfrac{-b}{a}$, and the midpoint of the roots is 5.4.

Since the midpoint of two numbers is half their sum, we know that $\frac{-b}{2a} = \frac{-b}{10} = 5.4$, giving $b = -54$. This makes the quadratic equation $5x^2 - 54x + 40 = 0$.

5. $\frac{x}{y} = 10$ gives $x = 10y$.

$\frac{x+5}{y} = 11$ gives $x + 5 = 11y$. Solve simultaneously to get $y = 5$, $x = 50$.

6. $\frac{40x - 120}{60} + \frac{6x}{60} - \frac{15 - 90x}{60} = 2$

$$\frac{136x - 105}{60} = 2$$

$$136x - 135 = 120$$

$$x = \frac{15}{8}$$

7. If we use the curve $y = \sqrt{x}$ to obtain the y-coordinates, then we get $(4, 2)$ and $\left(\frac{9}{4}, \frac{3}{2}\right)$ since we must remember that $\sqrt{x}$ means the positive square root of x. If, however, we use the line $y = 2x - 6$ to obtain the y-coordinates, then we get $(4, 2)$ and $\left(\frac{9}{4}, -\frac{3}{2}\right)$. This shows us that the only valid solution is the solution $(4, 2)$. The other solution arises when we square both sides of the equation: by changing the degree of the equation we introduce solutions that weren't originally there. Notice that the solution $\left(\frac{9}{4}, -\frac{3}{2}\right)$ would be correct if we were to take the negative square root. To see this more clearly, draw the graphs of $y = \sqrt{x}$, $y = -\sqrt{x}$ and $y = 2x - 6$ on the same set of axes.

8. $\frac{x^2 - 6x}{2x - 1} \div \frac{x - 6}{5} + \frac{4x}{1 - 2x} \equiv \frac{x(x-6)}{2x-1} \times \frac{5}{x-6} + \frac{4x}{1-2x}$

$$\equiv \frac{5x}{2x-1} + \frac{4x}{1-2x} \equiv \frac{5x}{2x-1} - \frac{4x}{2x-1} \equiv \frac{x}{2x-1}$$

9. $6y = 9x + 16$ gives $y = \frac{3}{2}x + \frac{8}{3}$. Perpendicular gradient is $\frac{-2}{3}$ so equation of l_2 is $y = \frac{-2}{3}x + c$. We know that c is at most $\frac{16}{3}$, giving us $y + \frac{2}{3}x \le \frac{16}{3}$. On the x-axis, $y = 0$ so we get $x \le 8$.

10. $(x + y)^2 = x^2 + y^2$ gives $x^2 + 2xy + y^2 = x^2 + y^2$ so $2xy = 0$, hence either $x = 0$ or $y = 0$.

11. There is no right or wrong answer here, but most people would check to see if the equation can be factorised first, then make a judgement on whether to use completing the square or the formula, depending on a number of factors. For example: What are the coefficients of the variables like? Can we use a calculator? ...). Decide on the decision process and, once your students are confident with the three techniques, give them ample opportunity to practise making good decisions.

12. This is true for any real number between 0 and 1.

Chapter 3

Try this first 3.1 (see the body of the text for more detail)

1. There are many ways including, but not limited to, a rectangular array, grouping objects, and skipping along a number line. It is left to the reader to decide how these might be interpreted for the other calculations in the question.

2. We know that the product of two negative numbers must be a positive number. An explanation of this is in the text.

3. Because this is a proportional relationship, which means the numbers change at the same rate and obey a multiplicative, not an additive, relationship.

3.1a

1. Each car has used a litre at the resting point. This is $\frac{2}{3}$ of the journey, so they can expect to use 1.5 litres in total. If one litre lasts for 40 km, then 1.5 litres lasts for 60 km, which is the approximate length of the journey (estimated since this is the *average* fuel consumption).

2. In 4 hours they would have built 1.5 walls (1 wall for the builder, half for the apprentice). The number of hours and the number of walls are in direct proportion, so we have 8 hours to build 3 walls, for instance. To build 2 walls takes $4 \div \frac{3}{2} \times 2 = \frac{16}{3} = 5\frac{1}{3}$ h, or 5 h 20 min.

3.1b

1. $a\%$ of b can be written as $\frac{a}{100} \times b \equiv \frac{ab}{100} \equiv \frac{b}{100} \times a$, which is $b\%$ of a.

2. There are three solutions. $x^3 = 0.64x$ gives:
$$x^3 - 0.64x = 0$$
$$x(x^2 - 0.64) = 0$$
$$x = 0 \text{ or } x = \pm\sqrt{0.64} = \pm 0.8$$

3. $m = 0.25n$, $n = 0.8p$ and $p = 0.25q$. This gives $m = 0.25(0.8(0.25q)) = 0.05q$. Rearrange to $q = 20m$. This means q is $20 \times 100 = 2000\%$ of m.

Try this first 3.2 (see the body of the text for more detail)

1. A ratio is another way of expressing the proportional relationship between two numbers. In the ratio $a:b$, the value of $\frac{b}{a}$ is the constant of proportionality.

2. If $a:b$ is equivalent to $c:d$, then $\frac{b}{a} = \frac{d}{c}$. This can be rearranged to give three other similar equations.

3.2

The fraction of students not bothered that they don't understand binary is $\frac{9}{13}$ of $\frac{10}{11}$, which is $\frac{9}{13} \times \frac{10}{11} = \frac{90}{143} \approx 62.9\%$. To split the '10' part of the ratio into 13 further parts, we need the LCM(10, 13), which is 130. Hence $1:10$ represents $13:130$ or 143 students as the smallest possible group size.

Try this first 3.3 (see the body of the text for more detail)

As one quantity doubles, the other:

a. doubles

b. is multiplied by 4 (2^2)

c. halves

d. is divided by 4 (2^2)

3.3

The line is given by $y = mx + c$. Since $m \propto c$ we know there is a constant, k, such that $m = kc$. To find where the line crosses the x-axis we put $y = 0$ and solve $kcx + c = 0$, which gives $x = \frac{-c}{kc} = \frac{-1}{k}$. This means the x-intercept of the line is fixed as the negative reciprocal of k. Use some online graphing software to see what this looks like.

Try this first 3.4 (see the body of the text for more detail)

Only you can answer this! There are many in the text.

3.4

1. $300\,000\,000\,\mathrm{m\,s^{-1}} = 3\times10^{8}\,\mathrm{m\,s^{-1}} = 3\times10^{5}\,\mathrm{km\,s^{-1}} = 3\times10^{-1}\,\mathrm{Gm\,s^{-1}}$

   $300\,000\,000\,\mathrm{m\,s^{-1}} = (3\times10^{8})\times3600\,\mathrm{m\,h^{-1}} = 1.08\times10^{12}\,\mathrm{m\,h^{-1}}$

   $\qquad\qquad = 1.08\times10^{18}\,\mathrm{\mu m\,h^{-1}}$

2. $\text{Distance} = (1.5\times10^{2})\times\dfrac{2}{3} = 1\times10^{2}\,\text{miles} = (1\times10^{2})\times1.6\,\text{km}$

   $\qquad\qquad = 1.6\times10^{2}\,\text{km}$

Quiz 3

1. This is exponential growth. Go back 1 day and the population is 14 million; go back another and the population is 7 million, which was after 6 days.

2. $(-1)^{n}$ is positive when n is even, and is negative when n is odd.

3. $6 = 6\times10^{0}$

4. Given $\dfrac{x}{y} = \dfrac{2}{1}$ and $\dfrac{x-3}{y-3} = \dfrac{9}{4}$, solve simultaneously to give original numbers 30 and 15.

5. The ratios 5 : 4 and 3 : 2 can be combined as 15 : 12 : 8 (boaters : berets : fedoras). This gives 35 parts. Since there are more than 50 hats in total, the smallest possible number of hats is 70, which is 30 boaters, 24 berets and 16 fedoras.

6. $\dfrac{(1\times10^{-6})+(2\times10^{-5})}{(430\times10^{4})-(2.2\times10^{6})} = \dfrac{(1\times10^{-6})+(20\times10^{-6})}{(4.3\times10^{6})-(2.2\times10^{6})} = \dfrac{21\times10^{-6}}{2.1\times10^{6}}$

   $\qquad = 10\times10^{-12} = 1\times10^{-11}$

7. $\sqrt{5} = 2+x$ so $5 = (2+x)^{2} = 4+4x+x^{2}$, giving $1 = x^{2}+4x$ and $\dfrac{1}{x} = x+4$.

   Reciprocating gives $x = \dfrac{1}{4+x}$. Putting this back into the original equation we have:

   $$\sqrt{5} = 2+\cfrac{1}{4+\cfrac{1}{4+\cfrac{1}{4+\cfrac{1}{4+\ldots}}}}$$

8. Let the number be x, then $\dfrac{1}{x} = x-n$ and $x = n+\dfrac{1}{x} = n+\cfrac{1}{n+\cfrac{1}{n+\frac{1}{n+\ldots}}}$.

   Also $\dfrac{1}{x} = x-n$ gives $1 = x^{2}-nx$, which rearranges to $x^{2} = 1+nx$ so

   $$x = \sqrt{1+nx} = \sqrt{1+n\sqrt{1+n\sqrt{1+n\sqrt{1+\ldots}}}}.$$

Chapter 4

Try this first 4.1 (see the body of the text for more detail)

1.
   a. geometric

   b. Fibonacci-style

   c. arithmetic

   d. quadratic

2. A term-to-term rule gets you from one term to the next one. A position-to-term rule gets you to a term if you know its position in the sequence.

4.1a

1. If we ignore the alternating sign, the sequence obeys the rule $2n+1$. Since the sign alternates we use the fact that even powers of -1 are positive and odd powers are negative. We want the odd terms in the sequence to be positive and the even terms to be negative, so $(-1)^{n-1}(2n+1)$ or $(-1)^{n+1}(2n+1)$ will do the job.

2. Each 'L' shape consists of one fixed circle in the bottom left corner. From this are two 'arms', which contain 1, 2, 3, 4, ..., n circles each. The two arms together therefore have $2n$ circles and, including the fixed corner circle, we have the sequence $2n+1$.

4.1b

In a cubic sequence the nth term is given by $an^3 + bn^2 + cn + d$.

Terms	$a+b+c+d$		$8a+4b+2c+d$		$27a+9b+3c+d$		$64a+16b+4c+d$
1st diff		$7a+3b+c$		$19a+5b+c$		$37a+7b+c$	
2nd diff		$12a+2b$			$18a+2b$		
3rd diff				$6a$			

In a quartic sequence the nth term is given by $an^4 + bn^3 + cn^2 + dn + e$.

Terms	$a+b+c+d+e$		$16a+8b+4c+2d+e$		$81a+27b+9c+3d+e$		$256a+64b+16c+4d+e$		$625a+125b+25c+5d+e$
1st diff		$15a+7b+3c+d$		$65a+19b+5c+d$		$175a+37b+7c+d$		$369a+61b+9c+d$	
2nd diff		$50a+12b+2c$			$110a+18b+2c$			$194a+24b+2c$	

3rd diff	$60a + 6b$	$84a + 6b$
4th diff	$24a$	

The second difference in a quadratic sequence is $2a = (2 \times 1)a$, the third difference in a cubic sequence is $6a = (3 \times 2 \times 1)a$, the fourth difference in a quartic sequence is $24a = (4 \times 3 \times 2 \times 1)a$, the pth difference in a sequence of degree p is $p!a$.

4.1c

Sequence name	p	Terms	nth term
Triangular	3	1, 3, 6, 10, 15, ...	$\frac{1}{2}n^2 + \frac{1}{2}n$
Square	4	1, 4, 9, 16, 25, ...	n^2
Pentagonal	5	1, 5, 12, 22, 35, ...	$\frac{3}{2}n^2 - \frac{1}{2}n$
Hexagonal	6	1, 6, 15, 28, 45, ...	$2n^2 - n$
Heptagonal	7	1, 7, 18, 34, 55, ...	$\frac{5}{2}n^2 - \frac{3}{2}n$
p-gonal	p	–	$\left(\frac{p}{2} - 1\right)n^2 + \left(2 - \frac{p}{2}\right)n$

The coefficients of n^2 and n in the nth terms each make a linear sequence, one increasing by $\frac{1}{2}$ each time and one decreasing by $\frac{1}{2}$ each time. The coefficients of n^2 are $\frac{p}{2} - 1$ and the coefficients of n are $2 - \frac{p}{2}$, which gives the general nth term for a sequence of p-gonal numbers.

Try this first 4.2 (see the body of the text for more detail)

1. Function notation enables us to describe the relationships between functions, especially when one function is a transformation or composition of others. '$f(x) =$' represents the function once applied to x, and '$y =$' represents the output of the function f(x).

2. Vertical asymptotes can be found by identifying when the denominator of a rational function is equal to 0. If we find the inverse of a function and can make its denominator equal to 0, then we have identified the location of a horizontal asymptote (on the original function). Oblique (slanted) asymptotes occur when the degree of the numerator is bigger than the degree of the denominator and can be found by polynomial division. This is beyond the scope of this book.

4.2a

1. Even functions are symmetric about the y-axis. Examples include $y = x^2$ and $y = \cos x$. Odd functions have rotational symmetry about the origin: if you rotate the function $180°$ it will fit onto itself. Examples include $y = x^3$ and $y = \sin x$.

2. The transformations are: translate by the vector $\begin{pmatrix} 2 \\ 0 \end{pmatrix}$, stretch horizontally by scale factor $\frac{1}{3}$, translate by vector $\begin{pmatrix} 0 \\ 1 \end{pmatrix}$. We know from completing the square that the minimum point of this quadratic is $\left(\frac{2}{3}, 1 \right)$. This tells us that the horizontal translation must take place before the horizontal stretch; if it happened the other way around the minimum point would be at $(2, 1)$. Generally, perform horizontal transformations first, and according to the reverse order of operations (adding/subtracting before multiplying), then perform vertical ones according to the order of operations. Try testing this out with some free online graphing software to see what happens more clearly.

4.2b

$x^3 - 2x + 5 = 0$ gives $x^3 = 2x - 5$ then divide by x^2 to obtain $x = \dfrac{2x - 5}{x^2}$ and the iterative formula $x_{n+1} = \dfrac{2x_n - 5}{x_n^2}$. From $x_0 = -2$ we get $x_1 = -2.25$, $x_2 = -1.88$, $x_3 = -2.49$, $x_4 = -1.61$, $x_5 = -3.16$, $x_6 = -1.13$, ... This rapidly diverges away from any root. A sketch of the graphs of $y = x$ and $y = \dfrac{2x - 5}{x^2}$ shows why this starting value does not work. There is no x_0 that will make this formula work.

$x^3 - 2x + 5 = 0$ gives $x^3 + 5 = 2x$, then divide by 2 to obtain $x = \dfrac{x^3 + 5}{2}$ and the iterative formula $x_{n+1} = \dfrac{x_n^3 + 5}{2}$. From $x_0 = -2$ we get $x_1 = -1.5$, $x_2 = 0.8125$, $x_3 = 2.77$, $x_4 = 13.11$, $x_5 = 1128.12$, ..., which again has diverged rather than converged. There is no x_0 that will make this formula work.

The reason the iterative formula given in the text worked, and these two did not, is because the curve was less steep than the line $y = x$. Specifically, if the gradient of the curve in the iterative formula is between -1 and 1, then the formula will work. In more advanced terms, using differentiation, we say that if $-1 < f'(x) < 1$ (1 being the gradient of the line $y = x$), then the formula will produce convergence.

4.2c

1. Only $f(x) + k$ would change the asymptote.

2. Considering $y = (-a)^x$, we know that we cannot apply an even root to a negative number ($\sqrt{-2}$, $\sqrt[4]{-7}$, etc.) and get a real number. So if x is a rational number with an even denominator, such as $\frac{1}{2}$ or $\frac{5}{4}$, the curve will be undefined at that point. Similarly, we cannot have an irrational power of a negative number. Consequently, the only points defined on the curve are those where x is a fraction with an odd denominator, which includes the integers (having denominator 1). This means the function is not *continuous*; you couldn't graph it as it would jump between positive and negative values, with plenty of gaps in between, and so we restrict our focus to positive bases only.

Try this first 4.3 (see the body of the text for more detail)

1. Since odd + even = odd, and 2 is the only even prime number, this is false only in the case that one of the prime numbers was 2.

2. Only you can answer this! There are some in the text.

4.3

1. Two consecutive even integers can be written $2n$ and $2n + 2$. The difference between their squares is $(2n + 2)^2 - (2n)^2 \equiv 4n^2 + 8n + 4 - 4n^2 \equiv 8n + 4 \equiv 4(2n + 1)$. This is a multiple of 4 but, more specifically, it tells us that this difference is always four times the odd number between the two original even numbers.

2. Two odd integers can be represented by $(2n + 1)$ and $(2m + 1)$. The difference between the squares of these two numbers is $(2n + 1)^2 - (2m + 1)^2 \equiv 4n^2 + 4n + 1 - (4m^2 + 4m + 1) \equiv 4n^2 + 4n - 4m^2 - 4m \equiv 4(n^2 + n - m^2 - m)$. We can see this is a multiple of 4. If we can show that the expression inside the bracket is even, then the whole expression is a multiple of 8. $n^2 + n \equiv n(n + 1)$, which must be even since it is the product of two consecutive numbers, one of which will be even. As a result the whole expression is a multiple of 8.

Quiz 4

1. In the picture in Figure A, we can see how one 'side' of the staircase can be removed and placed on the other side to create a square. This gives term 1 as a 2×2 square, term 2 as a 3×3 square, term 3 as a 4×4 square and term n as an $(n + 1)^2$ square.

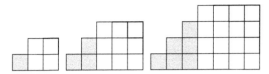

Figure A

To solve this algebraically, we have the sequence 4, 9, 16, 25, ... , which (if you don't recognise it as $(n+1)^2$) has first differences 5, 7, 9, ... and common second difference of 2, giving n^2 as the first term. Subtracting n^2 from each term in the sequence gives 3, 5, 7, 9, ..., which is a linear sequence with nth term $2n+1$. The nth term of the staircase sequence is therefore n^2+2n+1, which is the expanded form of the answer already given.

2. For rectangles we have the following.

Rectangle dimensions	Sequence	nth term
$1 \times n$	4, 7, 10, 13, ...	$3n+1$
$2 \times n$	7, 12, 17, 22, ...	$5n+2$
$3 \times n$	10, 17, 24, 31, ...	$7n+3$
$m \times n$	-	$(2m+1)n+m$

For cuboids we have the following:

Cuboid dimensions	Sequence	nth term
$1 \times 1 \times p$	12, 20, 28, ...	$8p+4$
$1 \times 2 \times p$	20, 33, 46, ...	$13p+7$
$1 \times 3 \times p$	28, 46, 64, ...	$18p+10$
$1 \times n \times p$	-	$(5n+3)p+(3n+1)$
$2 \times 1 \times p$	20, 33, 46, ...	$13p+7$
$2 \times 2 \times p$	33, 54, 75, ...	$21p+12$
$2 \times 3 \times p$	46, 75, 104, ...	$29p+17$
$2 \times n \times p$	-	$(8n+5)p+(5n+2)$
$3 \times 1 \times p$	28, 46, 64, ...	$18p+10$
$3 \times 2 \times p$	46, 75, 104, ...	$29p+17$
$3 \times 3 \times p$	64, 104, 144	$40p+24$
$3 \times n \times p$	-	$(11n+7)p+(7n+3)$
$m \times n \times p$	-	$((3m+2)n+(2m+1))p+((2m+1)n+m)$

3. a. geometric   b. Fibonacci   c. arithmetic (linear)   d. quadratic

4. As an example, the horizontal stretch given by $y = (2x)^3$ has the same effect as the vertical stretch given by $y = 8x^3$, since $2^3 = 8$. Generally, the horizontal stretch given by $y = (ax)^3$ has the same effect as the vertical stretch given by $y = a^3x^3$. If $f(x) = x^n$, then the stretches of $f(ax)$ and $a^n f(x)$ have the same effect.

5. $k(x) = 9x^2 - 6x + 1 \equiv 9\left(x^2 - \dfrac{2}{3}x + \dfrac{1}{9}\right) \equiv 9\left[\left(x - \dfrac{1}{3}\right)^2 - \dfrac{1}{9} + \dfrac{1}{9}\right] \equiv 9\left(x - \dfrac{1}{3}\right)^2$

The graph of $h(x) = x^2$ is translated by the vector $\begin{pmatrix} \frac{1}{3} \\ 0 \end{pmatrix}$ and stretched vertically by a scale factor of 9, so $k(x) = 9h\left(x - \dfrac{1}{3}\right)$. In this case, the transformations could be performed in either order with the same effect. If there was an extra horizontal or vertical transformation, then the order would matter. As mentioned in the solution to Problem 4.2a, convince yourself of this, using some online graphing software.

6. a. $((a+b)^2 + b^2)((a-b)^2 + b^2)$
   $\equiv (a^2 + 2ab + 2b^2)(a^2 - 2ab + 2b^2)$
   $\equiv a^4 - 2a^3b + 2a^2b^2 + 2a^3b - 4a^2b^2 + 4ab^3 + 2a^2b^2 - 4ab^3 + 4b^4$
   $\equiv a^4 + 4b^4$

   b. $7^{12} + 2^{2018} = (7^3)^4 + 2^2 \times 2^{2016} = (7^3)^4 + 4 \times (2^{504})^4$, which is of the form $a^4 + 4b^4$, where $a = 7^3$ and $b = 2^{504}$. This factorises, using Sophie Germain's identity and is therefore not prime.

7. $f(x) = \dfrac{x^3 - 3x^2 + 2x}{x^4 - 16} \equiv \dfrac{x(x^2 - 3x + 2)}{(x^2 - 4)(x^2 + 4)} \equiv \dfrac{x(x-2)(x-1)}{(x-2)(x+2)(x^2 + 4)}$

   $\equiv \dfrac{x(x-1)}{(x+2)(x^2 + 4)}$

   The denominator is equal to zero when $x = -2$, so this is the vertical asymptote. There is also a horizontal asymptote – as $x \to \pm\infty$, $f(x) \to 0$, which we know because the degree of the denominator is bigger than the degree of the numerator, so the horizontal asymptote is the line $y = 0$. Interestingly, the graph does cross this asymptote, as $f(x) = 0$ when $x = 0$ and when $x = 1$.

8. $f(x) = x^2 + 2x + 3 = (x+1)^2 - 1 + 3 = (x+1)^2 + 2$. Since a square number is always greater than or equal to zero, $f(x) \geq 2$ for all real values of x (which means $f(x) > 0$, which was the result to be proved).

9. When x is 0 in the equation $x^2 + y^2 = 1$, y is ± 1. If we add 1 to x and consider $(x+1)^2 + y^2 = 1$, then an input of −1 would have the same result. Generally, in this new equation, every value of x we enter will produce the same output as an x value one higher in the original equation. This means every point on the curve is located one to the left of every point on the original curve.

Similarly, when y is 0 in the original equation, x is ± 1, and if we subtract 1 from y and consider $x^2 + (y-1)^2 = 1$, then an input of 1 would have the same result. Every value of y we enter will produce the same x value as a y value one less in the original equation. This means every point on the curve is located one higher than every point on the original curve.

Combining these two effects gives a transformation by the vector $\begin{pmatrix} -1 \\ 1 \end{pmatrix}$.

10. Since $f(x)$ and $f^{-1}(x)$ are reflections in the line $y = x$, then any point of intersection must also lie on this line. We then know that we can find out when $f(x) = f^{-1}(x)$ by solving either $f(x) = x$ or $f^{-1}(x) = x$. The equation $f(x) = x$ is asking 'when does the output of f equal the input?'

Index